*The Valiant* 7

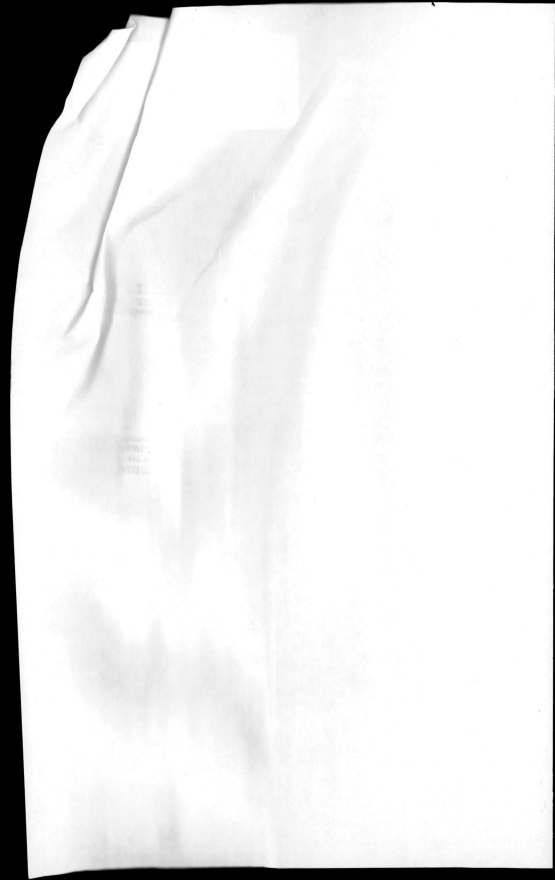

# The Valiant Seven

## By Netta Sheldon Phelps

ILLUSTRATED BY
HELEN HUGHES WILSON

## Caxton Classics

*CAXTON PRESS*
Caldwell, Idaho

2001

First Printing January, 1941
Second Printing January, 1942
Third Printing January, 2001


ISBN 0-87004-410-9




COPYRIGHT 1941 BY
THE CAXTON PRINTERS, LTD
CALDWELL, IDAHO

Printed and bound in the United States of America
*CAXTON PRESS*
Caldwell, Idaho
166743

DEDICATED TO THE YOUNG PEOPLE
OF THE GREAT NORTHWEST

## Foreword

AT THE time that the writer was serving as Regent of the Esther Reed chapter of the Daughters of the American Revolution, it was ascertained that three survivors of the Whitman Massacre were in the city, and they were asked to address a chapter meeting. Their talk made such an impression upon the writer that she determined to embody the long-ago experiences of these pioneers in a permanent form.

The only ambition the writer cherished was that every incident should be absolutely true; and to that end every situation and every conversation—save some half dozen of the latter—has been based upon the writings or the oral testimony of the several Sager girls who survived the massacre. The writer had the privilege of hearing, while they were still living, the stories of Catherine (Sager) Pringle, Matilda (Sager) Delaney, and Elizabeth (Sager) Helm. Clark S. Pringle, husband of the oldest sister, himself a member of the volunteers that scoured the Spokane country in search of the murderers, also aided with his clear remembrance of bygone days.

NETTA SHELDON PHELPS

# Contents

# Illustrations

The Valiant 7

# Chapter 1

# *Westward Ho!*

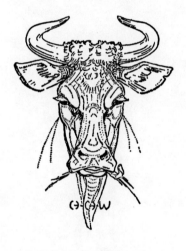

THE BIRDS had hardly uttered their first drowsy cheeps when the occupants of the camp began to stir. First one sleepy, tousled head would appear, from either a tent or wagon, then another, until finally the early morning shadows were peopled with boys and girls, fathers and mothers, intent on getting everything in readiness for the start. For today was the great day when the little company was to start on its long, long journey across the wilderness to Oregon. It was a long way from St. Joseph, Missouri, to Oregon, in oxcarts or on foot, but the promise of free land and a new start in life moved these pioneers, as all pioneers, to undertake the hard journey.

"I don't see why this fire acts so hateful," said John Sager, stirring it impatiently. "It burned all right yesterday. I s'pose it's because we're in such a hurry! Can't you find some drier stuff than this, Frank?"

"Hain't got time. Do your own huntin'," was his brother's ungracious response. "Pa told me to take down and roll up the tent, and the pesky ropes are all tangled; and if I don't get them straight, so the tent can go up in a hurry when we get to the camping place tonight, we'll get into trouble."

It was no easy job to break camp. The tent must be rolled, chairs forming a support for the wagon's endboard (converted at mealtime into a table) must be put in their places, and the various utensils packed safely away.

The great, strong wagon which was to carry the Sagers westward had a heavy load to carry. In the roomy back space was placed first a layer of bacon and dried meat, then the flour—wheat and rye, the cornmeal, peas, and beans, and many other staples. On top of these eatables was piled most of the bedding, the three or four feather beds that crowned the pile almost touching the canvas covering above. In front of these, thus dividing the wagon in two parts, was a stout chest containing the precious things of the family—those which could not be left behind them in St. Joseph: a very few books, a treasured picture or two, the better portion of the clothing, and a small store of crockery. On the right-hand side was a small space reserved for the churn, which occupied the corner. It was secured in its position by straps, and when the cows were milked night and morning the milk was strained directly into it, the person doing it standing upon the tongue of the wagon. Behind this stood a half cask to carry the precious water, and behind this in turn was a bushel basket in which were carried the pewter and tin dishes used upon the trip, for more fragile dishes would have been useless.

On the left-hand side of this front space was a portion reserved for the small supply of firewood that would have to be carried from one camp to

another, since no wagon train dared trust entirely
to good luck in finding it close at hand. On the remaining floor space and over the wood was placed
the tent and some of the older bedding; and on this
would sit Mrs. Sager, the mother of the family,
and the little girls, safely shut in by the high front
endgate, which Mr. Sager insisted upon in order to
keep the restless youngsters from falling out of
the wagon.

Rising in arches upon the sides were strips of
tough wood called wagon bows, and over them was
thrown the canvas that kept off the sun and rain
but could exclude neither heat nor cold. Hooks at
intervals on these strips were utilized to hang
many a thing for which there was no safety on the
wagon bottom. Mr. Sager's guns were slung in
loops of cloth from them. From one swung the band-
box which contained Mrs. Sager's best bonnet.
From others, near the back end, hung gourds which
were used as dippers to drink from, and from one
dangled little Elizabeth's doll, Betty, hanging by
a string tied around her waist. To the inside of
the canvas covering—which, save for two round
peekholes at either end, entirely shut out the outside world—pockets were sewn to hold combs and
brushes and other small articles.

At the back of the wagon was the feedbox, but
as the Sagers were not taking any horses, it was
used as a place to carry the very long-handled,
three-legged skillet, the Dutch oven, and other

cooking utensils. On this were also piled and tied several chairs.

On one side of the outer wagon body was fastened the toolbox, and on the other, the tent poles. From a long pole underneath the wagon swung the water pail and the tar bucket.

Mrs. Sager and the little girls—Catherine, or "Sis," aged nine; Elizabeth, seven; Tilda, five, who had to use crutches because of a knee left lame by a bone disease; and Hannah Louisa, three—took their places within the big wagon. John, aged fourteen, and Frank, aged ten, started off with the stock, and finally, with a creak and groan, the big wheels turned, and the Sager family was off to Oregon.

It was only a short distance to the Missouri River, and there the real business of the day began. First, one big wagon was carefully let down the little pitch that led to the big flatboat tied to the shore. While the oxen were taken off and sinewy hands grasped the tongue, others held stout ropes placed around the axles; slowly and carefully the big wagon home slid to a safe place on the boat. Then with lusty pulls at the ferry rope, boat and wagon made their slow, uncertain way across the river, which at that time was turbulent, with a strong current that swept the boat downstream.

None of the women and children went on the first boat but stood in a cluster on the top of the bank, eager spectators of the stirring scene.

Some of the men began at once the task of getting the stock across. Those who had horses used to the water would swim them across leading one or more not used to it, while with shouting and encouragement, those behind would drive the oxen and cows, and more horsemen would follow to prevent turning and retreat. But there were not enough horsemen to manage the stock, and some of the men had to undress and swim alongside the almost panic-stricken animals through the flowing water.

Back and forth many times went the weary men and horses, and wagon after wagon, group after group of stock, finally reached the western shore.

It was the middle of the afternoon before the Sager wagon took its turn at being safely lowered onto the big boat. As Mrs. Sager was not able to walk, she decided it was safer to be inside the wagon while on its river trip, so she and the little girls shut themselves within its canvas covering and listened fearfully and with bated breath to every strain and groan of the tough rawhide rope that held their boat against the onward rush of the turbid waters.

"I reckon I should swim like Tige does, if I should tumble out," said Elizabeth seriously, trying to peer out at a place where the canvas was not tightly fastened. "I s'pect it would be nicer to swim on the dry land, though, 'cause I ain't a fish. It would make your face cleaner, dolly," she continued, addressing the unimpressionable Betty, "and maybe you had better learn swimmin'."

"The little washtub is better for a little girl's bath, isn't it?" said her mother. "It's like some other things in this world—enough's enough—though some of us take some time and go through lots of trouble to find it out," she added to herself.

After a little, Tilda, with her bright eyes at the crack, exclaimed, "We're 'most acrost, and I can see Father and Tige on the bank!"

Mr. Sager had borrowed a horse and earlier had driven and coaxed Jake and Ike and the other oxen and cows belonging to him into the river, where, in spite of evident contrariness, they were forced

His hearty "Bowwow" was convincing.

to swim. Faithful Tige did his full duty in making them decide that the farther side of the river promised the best pasturage. His hearty "Bow-wow! Get along there!" was convincing. And when, after a little way out, they turned their eyes toward the receding bank to see if Tige had remained on shore and had, perhaps, gone off to chase a squirrel, if there wasn't that horrid dog *swimming!* Well, if Tige could swim as well as bark and bite, they might as well give up the point and go on, as he seemed to want them to do.

So, thanks to Tige's faithful generalship, Ike and Jake, Rock and Jolly, Buck and Barney were ready to pull the Sager wagon-home up the steep bank after the flatboat had touched the shore.

"Hurrah for Oregon!" exclaimed Frank, as he raced up the bank the minute it was safe to leave the boat. "Now we're really on the way! I wonder if we'll see any bigger rivers?"

"Maybe none wider," answered a man near him, "but we'll meet many a stream that hasn't any flatboat, and then how do you s'pose we'll get over?"

"Ford some of 'em, I reckon, and in the summer we'll not find 'em so high, perhaps. But I can't see what we'll do if we come across one of the big sort in a few days," answered Frank.

The little girls had by this time climbed out of the wagon and were running about eagerly, exclaiming with delight over a few spring flowers that had not yet folded their delicate white cloaks about them for the night.

"I wonder," said Sis thoughtfully, "if it's because the horses and cattle eat such pretty things like these flowers and violets and others, that their eyes are so beautiful!"

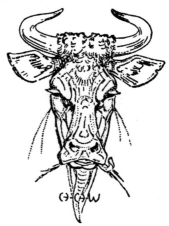

"Come on, children! Hurry up and climb in," said their father. We must hurry on, or night will overtake us before we can make camp."

John and Frank had already started with the stock, and in a very short time the big wagon was following the broad trail over the route taken earlier in the day by those that had crossed the river before them. Dusk was fast coming on when the short trip was ended by their finding those who had already arrived at the camping place where they were to remain until officers were chosen and rules and regulations governing their movements were determined upon.

It was thought best to observe care against hostile Indians even so early on the journey, so the wagons were formed into a circle. Then the children scattered to find fuel for the fires. This was not an easy task, for there had been prairie schooners stopping there before them; and it being so early in the spring, not much of the loose stuff they could find was dry. But they soon found enough to begin on, and before long the kettle was boiling, and supper was well under way.

"My, but I'm hungry!" said Mr. Sager, eating with the relish of a man who had been exercising all day. "I hope the rest of the company will have as good luck gittin' across the river as we did. If they all git over by day after tomorrer, we can start on in a couple of days after that."

"I'm going to wash everything that needs it, tomorrow," replied Mrs. Sager. "Then the day before we start, I can wash a little more. If this fine weather holds and I don't have a chill, I'll get everything shipshape in four or five days' time."

A commotion among the cattle, feeding a short distance outside the ring of wagons, drew the attention of the family from their supper. Before Mr. Sager, the boys, or even fleet-footed Tige could reach them their stock was off like a whirlwind toward the river.

The Sager family looked at each other in despair! Where had they gone, these four-footed servants, the only hope between them and the far distant place they thought so much of, and without whose aid it would be impossible for them to cross the trackless plains between the Missouri and far-off Oregon.

"Here, Sager, take my horse and follow them," called a cheery voice. "If we can only catch Dick in a hurry, mebbe you can head them off before they reach the river."

But Dick, although hobbled and near at hand, had caught the infection of restlessness from the cattle and it was some minutes before he was caught and the bridle put on. Mr. Sager mounted and rode off, shouting a reassuring word over his shoulder: "Don't worry, wife, if I don't come back before some time tomorrer. I'll foller the pesky things till I git 'em, no matter how long it takes me."

A minute more and he disappeared in the gloom of the evening.

"Now, Mis' Sager, don't you worry none," said the neighbor who had loaned the horse. "He may be back in the mornin' but more'n likely not before he chases them way back to yer old home in the bottom. Cattle is most as contrary as pigs, and pigs is the contrariest critters goin', unless ye reckon on these here women what's beginnin' to make so much talk 'bout the laws bein' all wrong, jest because the men make 'em."

"Well," replied Mrs. Sager with a smile, "I wish our cattle had not taken it into their heads to get

Mr. Sager mounted and rode off, shouting a reassuring word over his shoulder.

contrary just at this minute. Do you think we will be perfectly safe here tonight?"

"Bless yer, yes. What's goin' to harm ye? I'm goin' on guard, anyway, an' I'll keep special lookout in your direction. We'll be fixed jest the same as we will be every night till we git to Oregon, I s'pose."

He went on: "Yer see the wagins is already put in a tight circle, with the tongue of one run under the body of the one afore it, and then there's the herders outside with the cattle so nothin' will git very near and we not know it. Later on, when we git into the real Injun country, we'll have to do a leetle different. There'll be two sets of guards; the first set'll turn in at midnight or a leetle later, and the other'll keep watch the rest of the night. Tomorrer we're goin' to elect our officers and begin the drill, so that if the need comes we can face trouble and know how to do it, quick, too. I'll help the boys pitch yer tent, and then ye can turn in without a mite o' fear."

"Thank you so much," said Mrs. Sager gratefully. "I am thankful we are to have such kind and helpful neighbors on this hard trip."

In a few minutes the tent was up and everything ready for the night. Just as the dusk turned into darkness, the guards took their places outside the circle of wagons and grazing animals.

The campfires, built just inside the circle of wagons, smoldered and died down, though here and there one flared up and lit the faces of the circle about it. Young men and old sat about, and the women and older children formed groups here and there. The damp of the early spring was in the air, and with it the faint, sweet smell of violets and other wild flowers came up from the bank of the creek near by.

The sound of a fife, on which someone was practicing "calls," did not seem to disturb the quiet of the evening hush.

"Mother," said a sleepy voice in the Sager wagon, "isn't it nice to have that music along? If it was always like this, I'd just as lief live in a wagon all the time."

It seemed but a wink of time until the night shadows were driven away by the sun, and the promise of another beautiful day spread itself glowingly over the eastern sky. Regular rising time had not been determined upon as yet, the leaders who would guide the movements and make the rules for the party not having been chosen. Many of the travelers were so tired with the arduous work of the previous day that they were glad to indulge themselves with an extra nap this morning. Still, at five o'clock, many were astir, gathering wood and starting fires for breakfasts.

"Hello there! Get up! Get up! Get up!" followed by a burst of laughter, was the first thing John and Frank Sager heard in their tent. They hurriedly unrolled themselves from their old comforters and homespun blankets and stuck their heads out, thinking it might be their father returned with the wandering stock. No one was in sight. Their own wagon was shut, as was the one ahead of it and the one behind. Who was calling them? Again came the voice, "Good mornin'! Get up! Get up! Lazy boys!"

The boys looked at each other in amazement. Who was calling to them? They weren't lazy, anyway!

Suddenly a boy about their own age came tumbling out of the tent nearest them and looked at them pleasantly. "Wonderin' who's calling you-uns? 'Tain't nothin' and nobody but Minister Garish's old parrot. She's shet up in the wagon jest ahead of yourn. It's lots of fun to hear her chatter. Sometimes when the wagon tips in a hurry, she gets scared and will scream out, 'O my! O my! O my!' Mis' Garish is orful 'fraid she'll hear bad talk and learn to swear on the trip. I rather think she will, too, 'cause yest'day, I heerd her a-sayin' somethin' kinder softlike to herself, and it sounded like 'golly!' Then she'd laugh and say it agin an' laugh some more; over and over she'd do it, laughin' like she was orful tickled. Mis' Garish come around after a while an sorter half heerd her. 'What's that? What's that, Polly?' she'd say, and Polly kinder ducked her head and said, 'O my! Polly wants a cracker,' and then she laughed and laughed and whistled all to herself."

Just then Mrs. Sager untied the end of the wagon cover and descended to the ground, the little girls following, all but Tilda, whose lameness prevented her getting out alone. Frank sprang to assist her, for he was especially attached to his little sister and was her willing knight on every occasion.

"How do you feel this mornin'?" he inquired as he lifted her down.

"Oh, ever so good." replied Tilda, "Only I'm hungry. What do you think, Brother? Mother says I can have some chickens, all my very own, when we get to Oregon. Did Papa come back?"

The women washed clothes in the creek.

"Ain't seen nothin' of him," answered Frank. "Shouldn't wonder if he'd hev ter go a long ways 'fore he catches 'em."

"I wish he'd come," said the mother, "but let us hope he will be here before night."

# Chapter 2

# *The Young Hunter*

THE DAY was spent by the campers in making last preparations for beginning the real journey. The women washed clothes in the creek, while the men prepared their guns for hunting.

In the evening a meeting was called to elect leaders for the journey. A drummer was chosen to roll an awakening signal each morning. Although Mr. Sager had not yet returned he was elected one of the officers, and Mr. Shaw, a soldier of no small experience and reputation, was made captain.

Captain Shaw took his responsibilities and honors very quietly, but at the same time he showed that he was equal to the occasion by rising to his feet, after the officers had all been chosen, and proposing that, as there was time before dark, it might be well to have a little military drill. "We won't need much, but the time might come we'd need that little bad," was his remark. "And when we get out on the trail—after we've tramped miles and miles in a day—we won't feel like drillin' when night comes."

So in a few minutes the children were watching the men march and countermarch to the clearly called commands of Captain Shaw. It was truly, from a military point of view, an awkward squad; but keen, honest, earnest faces rose above the long legs, short legs, and ill-poised bodies, and by the time the night guard went on duty, a very fair understanding of simple military tactics had crept into the minds of most of the men.

The fifer sat long by the dying embers, practicing softly.

The fifer sat long by the dying embers, practicing as softly as he could the calls he would be required to give every day.

Next morning John Sager woke early. Hastily slipping into his outer garments and boots, he took his precious gun and quietly stole out of the tent without awakening the younger Frank. His mother had given her consent for him and young Nichols, one of the neighboring camp boys, to go hunting. They hoped to get an antelope.

It was chill and cold, and in the dim light John could make out the forms of some of the guard, pacing back and forth. The stock were beginning to arouse themselves from their night's rest, begin-

**Out of the mist and dimness of the early light came four slim animals.**

ning to forage for their breakfast in the rather scanty but nutritious prairie grass, now springing green and pleasant to the taste in the spring weather.

Just then young Nichols made his appearance, and following his pointing finger, the two boys hurried off in the direction of the creek.

They stopped a moment to exchange greetings with the guard. "Hain't heerd a livin' thing sence I come out here-a-ways," was his cheerful report. "Mighty oninterestin', I tell yer. The birds even hain't got to yippin' yit. Seems like it orter be most breakfast time."

"Jest ketch ahold on yer appetite and rastle with it until we git back, an' mebbe we'll bring ye some antelope to eat," suggested young Nichols.

"Huh! More'n likely it'll be woodchuck or skunk or some sech, 'stead of venison," rejoined the guard discouragingly.

The two boys hurried on and finally halted about a mile away in a clump of scrub bushes. They peered here and there hopefully, but seeing nothing had come to the conclusion that they had better go on farther, when, not a hundred feet away, out from the mist and dimness of the early light, came four slim animals. Quietly, without a sound, they were picking their leisurely way down to the creek for a drink.

John's heart leaped. Could it be that they two, of all that company of skilled hunters back there with the tents and wagons, were to be the first to capture some large game? Doubtless they would all be getting some later on the trip, but to be the first! His fingers tightened their grip and slowly, noiselessly, his gun came into position. The antelope were entirely unaware of them. The light breeze blew directly into the faces of the boys, so no warning human scent reached them.

Even if they had seen the hunters, their unconquerable curiosity would have prompted them to remain momentarily quiet, until their sensitive muzzles had asked innumerable questions.

John's companion almost imperceptibly motioned him to take the animal at their right, while he himself aimed his long-barreled gun at the leader of the little band. The two reports came as one, and the leader fell; two fled swiftly as shadows, while the one that John shot bounded convulsively a few steps and then fell, struggling feebly. A quick, merciful slash with young Nichols' hunting knife ended its life.

"There!" said John exultingly. "The old hunters may get all they want now—we've got the first ones! I rather guess Mr. Chamberlain won't tease me any more about my new gun being a good thing to plant and raise guncotton from!"

"We've got 'em beat this time, sure," said Nichols. "I'm mightily surprised, too. I didn't expect to see anything larger than a sage hen."

With an air of importance the boys shouldered

their kill and made their way back toward camp, where already, though it was still very early, the campfires were beginning to glow.

As they came in sight, one of the Eads boys sang out, "Where hev you fellers bin, and whose calves hev you bin a-killin'?"

"Call 'em calves, do yer? That shows that ye're nothin' but a farm galoot. S'pose we got 'em by standin' still and callin', 'Bossy, Bossy! Nice Bossy! Come let us play with yer'?" said Nichols in derision. "You'll hev to git up a bit earlier than yer did this mornin', if ye're goin' to eat this kind of veal!"

"Oh, wal," drawled Eads, "if it comes to short rations, it's share and share alike, I guess, and I won't need to go hungry with sech mighty hunters along."

"Well done, boys," said Mr. Shaw, who had come down to water his stock. "I'm glad we have two such good hunters with us. Your mother will be proud of you, my boy," he said, turning to examine John's trophy closely.

"You see my shot didn't kill right off, like it should have," said John modestly.

"Touch of buck fever, hey? Well, you'll soon get rid of that," was the kindly response, as the boys started on in the direction of camp.

Mrs. Sager was surprised and pleased with the result of John's morning venture. "That looks as if we had someone to look out for us, even if Father is not here," she said. "I do hope he will come to-day; if he doesn't, I shall surely begin to think something has happened to him."

The two animals were quickly dressed, and venison steak, instead of the bacon from their stores, made part of the Sager breakfast. A portion was given to the kind neighbor who had been supplying them with milk since the running away of their cows.

Soon after breakfast, while the morning was still young, a number of the men set out with dogs and horses to try their luck at hunting. Of course John, having no horse, was forced to remain in camp.

The days passed quietly, enlivened now and then by a game of "leap frog" or "stick knife" for the boys. The little girls took turns in helping with household duties, washing dishes, and putting them away. Mrs. Sager spread out the bedding to air in the sunshine before rolling it up in the wagon. On other mornings, when the order of the day was to be up before daylight and off at the word of command, their half-cooked breakfast having been swallowed hastily, this observance of good housekeeping would have to be foregone.

After a few hours the hunters returned. Several had deer and a few had surprised the wary partridge, while several rabbits hung at different saddlebows, the long ears, once so quivery and alert, swaying idly with the motion of the horse.

One of the hunters brought Mrs. Sager a rabbit

and two partridges, saying hastily to avoid her thanks, "Oh, that's all right. Mebbe Sager will hev luck some day when I haven't any."

"I wish he would come," said Mrs. Sager. "I'm thinking maybe he can't find the stock, and what we should do in that case, I don't know."

"Oh, well, don't worry. I expect he'll be along soon now."

"I wonder if that ain't Tige's bark?" said Frank excitedly, a moment later. "Seems to me it sounds just like him, when he says to Rock, 'Jest you move along quick now, or I'll make hash of your heels.'"

Sure enough, there they were, the truants, with Mr. Sager following.

"He's got 'em all!" cried Tilda. "There's Ike and Jake, Rock and Jolly, and Buck and Barney beside the other stock. Now we can go tomorrow with Captain Shaw and the rest." The little girl leaned against the wagon and waved her crutch excitedly.

There had been some talk among the men, who were impatient to be moving, of going on in the morning, leaving the Sager family to join another train, or overtake them by forced marches when Mr. Sager should return. Mrs. Sager had dreaded to be left behind, though she felt that she had no right to object; and great was her relief at seeing her husband approach.

"Where do you suppose the rascals went?" Mr. Sager asked, when he had come up and turned the weary stock over to John and Frank. "Clean back to the bottom! They must have run like so many antelope part of the way, to keep ahead of the horse. But I didn't give 'em much time to play once I caught up with 'em, and I hurried 'em back so fast I reckon they won't want to start off agin tonight."

# Chapter 3

# Rolling Wheels

The little girls helped one another dress.

THE DECISION was made to start off the next day. It seemed to John that he had hardly got into bed, when the loud rumble of the drum awakened him. A vigorous shaking by his smaller brother helped in the process, and in a few minutes, the fire was blazing and the boys were off with the stock to the creek.

Mrs. Sager attended to breakfast, while the little girls helped one another to dress. Mr. Sager rolled up the bedding and tent and stowed them safely away. Not long after five o'clock the entire family was ready for breakfast. Twenty minutes was allowed for the meal and ten minutes for washing and stowing away the dishes. Then with Rock and Jolly and the two other yokes of oxen hauling the wagon, and the boys driving the other animals, they pulled out, the fourth or fifth wagon to leave the circle.

The mother and the little girls were shut into the capacious depths of their canvas house. It was not so nice as being out in the fresh air, but there was a peekhole at either end, and not being able to walk, Mrs. Sager felt it safer to keep her daughters with her.

It was a sight full of interest to see the various families fall into line. Some had two or three wagons fastened one behind the other. The morning sunlight falling on the white tops made a pretty picture. There was frantic scrambling that morning to be off. In some cases, dishes and babies were hustled in indiscriminately, in order to pull out as near the head of the line as possible; for if the old adage regarding the devil and the lagging one did not apply here, it certainly might have been truthfully said, "*Dust* takes the hindmost!" In all, there were about one hundred and fifty wagons.

The wagon behind the Sagers' was driven by the Rev. Mr. Garish, a Methodist minister, who, not being as experienced a driver as might be, was, in spite of the best intentions in the world, continually getting into difficulties. The trail, filled with holes and sidings, was none too good. During the trip, his frequent mishaps called out many remarks from his fellow travelers.

"Huh!" exclaimed an irreverent youth upon one occasion. "If that there's the way Parson Garish guides folks to Heaven, the way he's drivin' them air steers, I'd be afeered to yoke up to his religious wagin. When it comes to steerin' twixt Heaven and the tother place, you've jest natchully got to think quick, and know right from left without takin' too long to pray over it."

This particular morning, his wagon did not quite upset, but came near enough it to excite the parrot. "Laws a-massy, hold on, hold on!" screamed Polly, as with ruffled feathers, she swung and balanced on her bar. "Let us pray! Let us pray!" she con-

"Laws a-massy, hold on, hold
on!" screamed Polly.

tinued, as with a desperate lurch the steers drew
the wagon from the hole. Then the little girls in
the Sager wagon heard her give an infectious
laugh, a sort of long drawn out chuckle, ending
with a sanctimonious "O Lord! O Lord!" as she
became tranquilized by the steadier motion of the
wagon and fell to smoothing her disturbed feathers.

It grew warmer and dustier as the morning went
on and when about eleven they came near a small
brook, it was decided to stop and rest until one.
What a relief it was to get out of the big wagon,
and how the little girls darted here and there in

an effort to "limber up their aches," as Sis said.

There was no formation of the circle at noon, but each wagon stopped in line, and while the stock cropped a light lunch by the wayside, the cold dinners were taken out and hastily eaten.

"You'd think of somethin' else besides your aches, if you had our job," said Frank. "S'pose you let us ride and you drive the stock for a while."

"I'd just like to if mother would let me," answered Sis. "It would be lots better than being shut up all the time."

"Can't I drive the oxen a little while this afternoon?" asked John of his father.

"Well, mebbe. A few of us are goin' to hunt a little and if you think you can be very careful, you may start, if I'm not back in time. We'll take jest a leetle trip while the folks are restin'. Don't reckon to find much this time o' day, but we'll see what's near us."

"Why, Henry, you don't think there are Indians around, do you?" asked Mrs. Sager anxiously.

"I reckon there may be, but they won't hurt anybody," answered Mr. Sager easily. "You'll see lots of 'em before you git across the plains. They're quite decent sort of folks, unless they git mad, I'm told. Wust thing about 'em is, that the oxen don't like their looks or the smell of 'em, one or the other, and some bolt if they come around too near. That's what some of the men tell me. Ain't so bad as buffalo for that, though, they say."

"I heard a woman tell Mrs. Chamberlain that sometimes a herd of buffalo will run right over a wagon and break everything to pieces, 'fore the people can get out of the way," said Sis. "She said some old trapper told her so."

"There are many ways of turning a herd, so don't be skeered afore you're hurt," rejoined her father.

After lunch was eaten, many availed themselves of the opportunity to take a short nap before going on. Some spread comforts in the scanty shade offered by the wagons and slept in spite of all the camp noises; others merely threw themselves on the ground and seemed to sleep just as comfortably.

Soon the hunters returned, with Mr. Sager among the fortunate ones who had brought back some game. This was hastily dressed, sprinkled with salt, and stowed away to serve for the evening meal. Then the oxen were quickly yoked to the wagon and the westward way resumed.

The afternoon sun shone down warm on the canvas cover, but the little girls forgot the uncomfortable motion and heat in little naps which came to them as they sprawled on the bedding. Even Frank came and curled up for a snooze and after he was rested, John came for a while, his brother taking his place in driving the stock. The cattle were tired enough now to go along quietly, only stopping now and then to snatch a hasty mouthful of prairie grass. At five o'clock a halt was called beside a little creek.

As this was the first night on the trail, the order of formation was decided upon. The first wagon stopped at a certain point indicated by Captain Shaw, the team following being brought up as near as possible. When the oxen were out of the way, the second wagon was pushed by hand near enough to the first so that its tongue was partly underneath the body of the one ahead. By continuing in this way as each came up, there was formed a compact circle which would be hard to "rush." Though neither Indian nor buffalo would have been deterred from making a rush had they desired to do so, they both would have comprehended in their own way, that here was something formidable and quite capable of opposing them; that behind the queer, ungainly-looking hulks could come, on a sudden, a bright light and a sting that it would be wise to avoid. Inside the circle of wagons, tents were pitched and campfires built, and the cattle, too, were driven inside it. This would prevent their being stampeded by some sudden fright.

After the cooking of the simple supper, the children played outside the wagon circle for a little while, then willingly came in to bed. After a few songs were sung around the campfires, the whole weary group took their way to bed. Only the guards on their beat disturbed the complete silence of the night.

## Chapter 4

# Buffalo Thunder

THE WAGON train moved slowly westward. When it came into the buffalo country of vast plains where no wood grew for miles together, the little girls had a new duty. It was to gather and stow away in bags the "buffalo chips," or dried droppings of these animals. It seemed a disagreeable task at first, but it was necessary. When thoroughly dried, these "chips" made a clear, hot fire, with next to no odor and little smoke. When it rained, as it did after a while, the task of cooking by this sort of firewood became a much harder duty.

"Every time I see a buffalo, I half expect to see an Indian, too," said Sally Chamberlain one day as she and the Sager girls were wandering on at a little distance from the wagons.

If they looked in any one of several directions, they could discern in the distance very plainly in the clear air, herds of these animals feeding on the bunch grass of the plains.

The size and number of the herds increased as the wagon train neared the Platte. Formidable looking animals they were, especially the bulls, with the huge mass of hair about their heads and shoulders and their sharp horns curved slightly outward and upward. The night guard was instructed to keep constant watch, for the officers of the wagon train feared a night stampede by the animals, who, when once headed in the direction of water or new feeding grounds, would sometimes push on, countless thousands strong, and no barricade of wagons could for an instant resist their onward rush.

Wagons, household goods, men, women, children, and animals would be ground to a pulp beneath the flying, relentless, unswerving hoofs of these migrants of the plains, who were both friend and

menace to the venturesome pioneer. A friend, because their flesh often served to put new strength into bodies hungering for fresh meat; and a menace, not only from the mischief a stampede might do, but from the fact that possibly hostile Indians often hovered in their vicinity.

However, the Indians were very quiet and friendly this year, so there was little fear on this score among Captain Shaw's party.

Late one afternoon the train halted by the side of a small creek and though it was not a very good place for camping, Captain Shaw decided they would not be likely to find a better one while daylight lasted. There seemed to be a sort of mud dam, not very skillfully made, but strong enough to hold back the rather scanty supply of water sufficiently to form a wallowing place for the bison. But there were none of the animals in sight, nor had there been for the last few hours, so Captain Shaw decided it would be safe to stop for the night.

Over the campfires the suppers were soon cooking, and afterwards games and singing took the time, until an early retiring brought sleep to tired bodies.

But after a time, the guards heard a strong, low, ceaseless, roaring sound, like waves breaking on some rocky coast. Startled, they watched and waited in the dimness of the starlit night for—they wondered what? The sound seemed to come nearer and directly towards the camp, and Captain Shaw, who had been called, quickly decided that it was a herd of buffalo on one of their rapid and irresistible journeys.

Perplexity and responsibility showed plainly in the Captain's demeanor as, after listening a bit and deciding that the herd was surely coming in their direction, he directed that eight or ten of the men take their guns and go with him a little distance in front of the camp.

Mr. Sager and Mr. Chamberlain were of the party and with the others had hastily bridled the first horse they could lay hands on. It was not a

question of ownership, but a question of quickness
of movement and aim. The anxious little party
listened with strained nerves until, through the
gathering mistiness and the shadows that foretold
rain for the morrow, came the leaders of the herd.
They seemed to be heading a trifle west of the point
where the party stood in a rather widely separated
line. The guns rang out again and again and
though they were too distant to have the shots tell
and none of the huge animals fell, they swerved
slightly to the right and without changing their
speed, charged on into the gloom. For an hour the
little party of stalwart defenders stood their
ground; and then as the hoofbeats passed on towards the silence of the endless plains, they re-
traced their way to camp with thankful hearts.

"Tell yer what," said one. "I believe I'd ruther
fight Injuns than try to stop a herd of buffalo. The
Injun hez got a mite o' think to him, and yer stand
a show o' makin' him see that yer might be ez
dangerous ez he most ginerally is; but a buffalo
can't see but jest one thing, and that's mighty sure
to be the pint he's aimin' fer."

Before noon the next day, the party reached the
fording place of the River Platte. It looked a bit
formidable, but some Indians hovering near assured them by signs that this was the place where
they must cross. An inspection revealed the fact
that they could not cross directly, in a straight line
from shore to shore, but must follow with the

utmost care the tortuous turnings of a narrow, submerged ridge only as wide as a wagon, with a few inches to spare on either side. Beyond that, the river bed shelved abruptly into deep water and quicksand. In order to make sure of the safety of the wagons, they were fastened two and two, one behind the other, to be taken across. Several men waded in the cold water, two or three on either side of the wagons and one at the head of each yoke of oxen. It took much coaxing, hawing, and geeing to induce the oxen to keep to the narrow path; and the patience and nerves of all humans and animals were severely tried before the day was done. To Mrs. Sager, the nerve-racking crunch, crunch, of the wheels as they rolled slowly over the narrow wet trail of the river bed, was the most trying experience she had so far been called upon to endure. A slight deviation meant disaster in the quicksand so near at hand.

The Indians seemed absorbed in watching the exertions of the white travelers. The squaws and children clustered at a distance upon any slight elevation they could find, while the bucks came nearer, sitting motionless upon their ponies, listening intently to every word used to keep the nervous oxen up to their arduous work.

Finally the spirit of emulation, which at certain times is a marked characteristic of the Indian nature, grew too strong for some of them; and they rode their ponies into the water, trying their best to imitate the gestures and shouts of the white men.

It might have been amusing to those safely across, to see the dignified, statuesque figures turn suddenly into excited, vociferating madmen; but to the men whose task now became doubly hard to keep the excited oxen from bolting to one side or the other, and to the terrified women and children shut up in the big wagons, listening in tense silence to the sound of the loose gravel beneath the wheels, it was anything but amusing, this new terror, which held much of menace and possible disaster.

There was no such thing as asking the Indians to be quiet, for no one could speak a word they could understand; and if signs were made that they were to go away, it might affront and anger them to such an extent that they would suddenly turn hostile; so, perforce, their wild antics had to be endured. Fortunately, no accident occurred and when night came, camp was made safely on the farther shore.

"That's a good job done," said one of the men cheerily, pausing for a moment beside the Sager campfire. "I tell yer, I hope we won't have many more rivers like that one to cross!"

"If we do, let's pray we'll not have quite so much help about it! Them Injuns made me purty riled with their squawkin'," responded Mr. Sager.

Buffalo having become an everyday occurrence, the task of supplying fresh meat was an easy one. Some of the men who were good shots, like Mr.

The Indians rode their ponies into the water, trying their best to imitate the gestures and shouts of the white men.

Sager, would leave their wagons in charge of others and sally out hunting. Some days they could find buffalo only a few steps from the train, but at other times they had to go farther. If they had horses, it was comparatively easy to ride close enough to get a fair shot. With a little practice they were able to ride in among a small herd, select their victim and, galloping their horses alongside, fire until the huge animal dropped.

Sometimes the enthusiasm of the hunters led them to travel miles even on foot in pursuit. Mr. Sager, not having horses with him, was often forced to go on foot. But he was usually fortunate and nearly always brought back something, even if nothing larger than a rabbit. Antelope were often seen, but their wonderful fleetness of foot usually saved them. In fact, nothing but their insatiable curiosity could draw them near enough, or hold them still long enough, to become targets.

"Jest about like tryin' to hit chain lightnin'," grumbled John Sager. "You aim where the lightnin' starts in and by the time the smoke clears away, you'll find the antelope and all his relations are 'bout as far off as where the lightnin' stops— way of makin' some other part o' the horizon look interestin'." John's first antelope had been his only one up to this time.

The plain was at the height of its spring beauty. The buffalo grass was taking on the pale green tint that transformed, for a few weeks, that part of the world. Not many weeks of the scorching, withering summer sun would it take to change the waving green tufts to the brownish ones that would dry and cure and gain additional sweetness in the process. The flowers sprang up by hundreds and thousands, and to some they brought comfort and a seeming promise of good things ahead. The children made garlands of the fragrant blooms.

One night not long after the first buffalo scare there was another alarm from the migrating herds.

The night watch hastily called Captain Shaw and again the men went in the darkness, a little way from camp, to try to locate the head of the flying herd. With their hearts beating rapidly, they listened to a low monotone that momentarily grew stronger and stronger and gradually assumed the sound of a continuous roll of thunder. Would they run over the helpless train, or would they turn aside as before?

The tense moments crept by, each second hours long, and the rumble vibrated dully against the strained ears of the watchers. Once a light grew stronger, as the clouds, driven by a gentle wind, parted to let the men see the stars shining serenely.

"Seems to me," shouted Captain Shaw suddenly, "that the noise is goin' over yonder 'cross the creek."

"Don't crow too soon; nothin' but a plumb fool of a rooster will be stretchin' his neck to say 'Cock-a-doodle-do' at midnight," rejoined one of the men.

"Seems to me, the shadders and the noise is veerin' this way."

It seemed so at that moment, and Captain Shaw shouted, "Fire away, boys!" and a volley rang out. Again and again they fired, not daring to leave their post all night. The sunrise found them in their places, with the herd still passing.

But only a few days later, Captain Shaw's party came across some remains of a camp outfit, here and there tattered shreds of canvas and clothing, iron cooking utensils broken into small bits, pieces of wagon not larger than kindling wood, and two or three mounds of freshly heaped earth, which told their own sad story. As they learned long after, two or three wagons and their occupants had stopped in the path of the hurrying hoofs of a herd of buffalo; and when the herd had passed, little remained of humans, animals, or wagons. The train next behind had reverently buried what most resembled human remains and the rest of the wreckage told its pitiful tale to sun and wind, the moon and stars, the rabbit and the prowling coyote.

A few days of varying sun and storm succeeded this last experience, when one afternoon the children, skipping alongside near the wagon, heard their mother call to her husband and very soon their wagon drew out from the long line and stopped. The rest of the train passed on, leaving the Sager wagon behind.

"You go off and play by yourselves, children,"

said the father, lifting little Tilda out. "Look out
for Tilda and Hannah Louisa, Sis. You had better
keep right on with the other teams, though, I
reckon. We can see where they're goin' to stop
from here. We'll be along with the wagon after a
while."

"Yes, come along and camp with me," said a
woman on horseback, who had stopped for a few
minutes at the Sager wagon and was now hurrying
toward the camp. "I'll take little Hannah on my
horse and she can have a nice ride."

"And Tilda can come on my horse," said another woman, who had also stopped at the wagon.

Tilda didn't want to go and with her older sister
walked on for a little distance, stopping half the
distance between the wagon and the big camp,
where they began to play games in a halfhearted
sort of way. A little later, they saw Mrs. Shelton
and Mrs. Stuart returning hurriedly from the
camp to the Sager wagon, the former having a
little package that looked like medicine.

"Is Mother sick, Mrs. Shelton?" Sis called as the
horsewoman passed her.

"She ain't feelin' jest right, but you younguns
go on with your playin', or better yet, go on where
the rest of the wagons be. Jest give your ma time
to rest a spell and she'll be all right. I'll see to her
and don't you worry."

The rest of the afternoon passed very slowly for
the little girls, who could not persuade themselves

to go to the big camp, but stayed in the place they
had first chosen for a playground.

Finally their father came to them and directed
them to proceed at once to camp, saying he was
coming with the wagon in a short time.

They started, proceeding slowly on Tilda's account. After a time the wagon overtook them, but
did not halt as it reached them, continuing slowly
on its way.

As it passed them, they heard a faint cry, like
a tiny child crying. All at once Sis began to jump
up and down, her eyes shining with excitement.
"Oh! Oh!" she exclaimed, "I know something—
Mother's got a new baby!"

"Really?" cried Elizabeth. "Let's hurry on so

They heard a faint cry, like a tiny child crying.

we can see it! Maybe it'll be even nicer than Betty was!"

The reference to the doll Betty in the past tense came from the fact that there had been so much contention between Elizabeth and Tilda over her possession, and so many hard feelings and tears had resulted, that the father had decided Betty's absence would be conducive to added peace in the family. So the torn and tattered doll had been found missing one fine morning.

"But I hope if we've really got a new baby, we won't lose it like we did Betty," said Tilda.

It looked like rain that night when the campers went to bed, and by midnight it was raining hard. At first, some of the wakeful ones thought it was only a passing shower, as so many others had been. But one of the guards noticed that the creek near by was rising rapidly, and he awakened Captain Shaw. They found that all the hollows were filling with water, and it was considered necessary to give the word to move camp some distance back to higher ground. Otherwise the creek, which showed decided signs of becoming a river, might engulf them all.

In the meantime, many of those in tents woke up to find their bedding completely soaked. The water was already running in a stream through some of the tents.

## Chapter 5

# The Long, Long Days

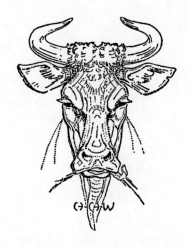

IT WAS a very bedraggled, uncomfortable company that resumed its way the following morning. A late start was made, many lingering to make a more or less unsuccessful effort to dry out things. But go on they must, sick or well, wet or dry.

Not even for birth or death could the emigrants tarry long by the way; for two or three days' delay might mean hunger and starvation to many, before the long trip ended; and to push west morning, noon, and night was the need, more and more imperative as the difficulties of the way stared them more plainly and unrelentingly in the face.

By common consent, the Sager wagon was this morning given a place very near the head of the train, so that the little family might be under the kindly supervision of the Shaws. The elements seemed to have spent their fury and for two or three days thereafter, sunshine and good weather prevailed. Mrs. Sager took a slight cold during the night of the downpour but as the days passed, nothing very serious seemed to follow.

In the meantime, animated discussions took place among the Sager children as to what name they should give the new sister. Tilda thought she should be the one to name her, for she would have to ride most of the time with her in the wagon, on account of the lame leg which was still not strong enough to allow her to do much walking. Finally the discussions ran so high that Mr. and Mrs. Sager took the matter into their own hands and decided that Henrietta was a good name for the little one.

On one or two occasions, men from the train ahead had waited for Captain Shaw's train to overtake them. They were, for some reason or other, dissatisfied and fancied they would find life easier in other company. Sometimes Captain Shaw's train was overtaken by someone from the train behind who hurried ahead in order to pay a friendly visit. So between the trains, which traveled two or three days apart, there was an occasional interchange of either discontented or curious visitors.

One of the migrations from the Shaw train to the one ahead caused some amusement and more or less comment.

In Captain Shaw's train was a young fellow, Frius Walkup by name. He had lost his heart to a young woman of the company and together they had toiled over the miles of prairie, planning for the home he would win for her from the wilderness. Doubtless to each the way was one of happiness, because they could see each other daily, and each camp song was more musical, each camp dance more enjoyable, because of the presence of the loved one. Everything went peacefully with love's young dream until one fateful evening. The young woman, who was quick-tempered, as well as a competent cook, mixed some biscuits and left young Walkup by the campfire to watch and see they did not burn in the Dutch oven. But alas! "The dreams of youth are long, *long* dreams," and his were longer than it takes biscuits to bake before an open fire. So when the cook returned, she found her lover still in a daydream and the biscuits burned black before his unseeing eyes. That was too much for her serenity of temper and then and there she broke the engagement.

She found the biscuits burned black.

Without waiting to hear the comments or questions of his traveling friends upon the situation, young Walkup early next morning took his clothes and pushed on to join the train ahead.

At the next stopping place, as many sat around the campfire, singing, repeating poetry, doing the many things suggested by the occasion, this poem was read by the camp poet.

On the twenty-first of June,
One morning very soon,
Frius Walkup arose
And called for his clothes.

While he was living with the Doctor,
He thought he bore the sway;
But by the burning of the biscuit,
He was forced to run away.

The reason of his leaving
No mortal man can say,
But by the burning of the biscuit
He was forced to run away.

A general laugh was indulged in by all but one blushing girl, whose blushes, however, did not prevent her eyes blazing with anger. But attention was drawn from her by the dry remark of an old man, "Now, boys, I tell yer this: whether it's apples in Eden or biscuits on the plain, it's a hull lot safer to let 'em alone an' let the wimmin do the cookin'."

As time passed, it was noted that the constant travel was beginning to wear on the horses and oxen. They had less strength and spirit for a hard pull, and when showers came, as they very frequently did, causing the trail to grow slippery and muddy, the oxen were very visibly discouraged. So it became necessary to go over the precious store of household goods and leave by the wayside some of the least necessary, in order to lighten the load. That the same necessity had come to other trains ahead of them was evidenced by heaps of abandoned household belongings at all the camping places. Sometimes it was a chair or a chest, sometimes dishes, kettles, or clothing. An occasional mound of earth warned them that sickness, too, and even death, lurked beside the trail. There were several cases of sickness in their own company by this time, and the way began to seem long to many.

One day after a heavy rain the trail grew very bad and the Sager wagon slid uncontrollably from one rut to another. Mr. Sager encouraged his oxen by his voice, and ran beside the wagon on the down side, supporting it as much as possible to keep it from tipping over. It was heavy, hard, uncertain work and told upon his strength, as it did upon that of the other drivers.

"My land!" said Mrs. Sager, as the wagon lurched far to one side, "I would walk if it wasn't for the baby, but I don't like to leave it and Tilda in the wagon alone. It might go over entirely and then who would save them from being hurt? I hope the way will be smoother after a time, but we can hardly expect it as we go towards the mountains."

Just then the wagon lurched again, farther than before, and the occupants, Mrs. Sager and the little girls, felt everything sway and slip for an instant, and then, quicker than it takes to tell it, over went the wagon right on its side. The occupants seemed to be underneath everything movable on top, the churn jammed down among the rolls of bedding, the box of dishes clattering upon the pork and the shoulders of ham. It was a wild scene that greeted

Mr. Sager's white face, as he tore open the front end of the canvas.

One by one he lifted the occupants out, willing hands from teams front and rear coming to help him.

"Naomi, Naomi, are you hurt?" he questioned, as no movement came from his wife, whom he could see with the baby clasped to her breast, lying under a pile of household articles, partly hidden by the feather bed on which she had been sitting. She did not answer, and the frightened husband forced his way to her side, took little Henrietta from her unresisting arms and then lifted the still form and crawled with it to the entrance, where others took it from him and laid it upon the earth by the side of the trail.

The children hushed their screams and gathered with awe-stricken faces to look upon the face of the dear mother lying so white and still. Could it be that Mother had left them—that her life had gone out so swiftly, without chance for one more loving word?

Mr. Sager stood by the side of his wife bewildered and dazed. "I *couldn't* help it, Naomi," he murmured over and over again. "It was so heavy that three men couldn't have kept it right side up. I tried my best."

"Jest you children stand back and let me git to her," said a capable, comforting voice, and a strong arm pushed the youngsters away and Mrs.

The frightened husband lifted the still form and carried her to the
entrance.

Shaw knelt beside the form of her friend, feeling her pulse and heartbeat. "She's still breathin', Mr. Sager, and you put up the tent if you can find it, and we women will do everything we can for her while you men straighten out that mess," indicating the overturned wagon.

The tent was found and quickly set up and the still unconscious form placed in it. The baby, who seemed uninjured, found shelter in motherly arms, while three or four women worked over the victim of the accident.

It was an hour before Mrs. Sager showed signs of consciousness, but not for a moment of that hour did her faithful friends relax their efforts. Camphor was hastily taken from more than one carefully packed medicine box and applied to nose and face; hands and feet were rubbed vigorously to restore circulation. Mr. Sager, who was nearly crazed by the accident, gave but scant attention to the repacking of his wagon. The children had miraculously escaped with a few minor bruises.

Finally Mrs. Sager's eyes opened, and she tried to sit up, looking around questioningly.

"The baby's all right and all the rest of 'em. Don't you worry none," said Mrs. Gilliam quickly.

"Did we go over, and is the wagon broken?" questioned Mrs. Sager.

"Yes, ye went over fast enough, but they've got things about put to rights now, I reckon. That bump comes from your hittin' somethin', don't it?

Well, wife, I believe you'd better drive and let me ride a while—I'd rather bump my head like you did, than be as scairt as I've bin for the last hour!" said Mr. Sager, so relieved to see his wife sitting up that he became almost jovial.

"Oh, I'm all right, only the next time we come to a bad place, just let me know and I'll get out and walk a while. I'm all ready to go on now. Such a pity that we should have delayed you all so," she said apologetically, to the women standing around. "But it's no use either to cry over this spilled milk or what I suppose is spilled out of my churn. Is every last thing ruined, Henry?" she continued, turning to her husband.

"No, not to say spiled, though between the spilled milk and the rain, fer it's bin a-showerin', things is some damp. But the wagon's not broken—that's the main thing. I've left out some things, Naomi, for the cattle seem to be gittin' kinder tired and I reckon it'll be best to lighten the load a mite. I've tried to leave the things we'll need least, but 'twas hard pickin'. We've *got* to have our victuals, so I've left off some chairs and the little old light-stand and some empty sacks that had had some of our groceries in."

"I hate to leave the chairs," said Mrs. Sager, "but I s'pose it's some better than leaving ourselves, and it might come to a question of doing that. That light-stand belonged to my mother, so I sure hate to leave it," and a sad look settled upon her face, as she passed it on her way to the wagon. "Good-by, old friend," she said, passing her hand caressingly over its marred surface.

The weather cleared and stayed clear for several days after that, but the sun became scorching. Camping places with plenty of water were far apart. The game, too, began to be scarce, owing to the lack of watering places, and the hunters had to go far and fast to obtain any. This diversion of hunting was a great relief to Mr. Sager, who enjoyed it thoroughly. In consequence, John and Frank became expert in driving the oxcart, for one of them had to turn teamster in their father's absence. As the oxen had by this time become used to their work, it was not so hazardous as at first.

"That old Rock knows just what I expect of him, the minute I look at him out of the corner of my eye," said John one day. They were ambling along in the heat, John driving and his father resting in the wagon, after a long, hot tramp after game. Sis went flying out of the wagon, thinking to walk a while.

Many of the children of the train, and some of the women as well, had become expert at getting in and out of the wagons without having the oxen stop their slow walk. A well balanced jump onto the tongue just behind the nearest yoke, then a leap past them and in front of the front wheel and they would find themselves on the ground. In getting into the wagon this was reversed.

As Sis reached John's side, she heard shouts of laughter and saw a wagon drawn by four oxen, running wildly out on the prairie outside the line of the train, but in the same direction they were going.

"Jingo!" said John. "Aunt Becky is tryin' a new kind of travelin'. How them oxen do go it!"

It was a funny sight and laughter was perhaps excusable under the circumstances, for seated astride of the tongue was a frightened-looking woman, clinging desperately to the straight wooden piece upon which she sat, her sunbonnet dislodged from her head and hanging back on her shoulders, wisps of straight hair flying in the breeze, and her calico dress fluttering. The oxen seemed bent on going their own sweet way and the efforts of a young boy who had been driving were now confined to clinging to his seat on the front of the wagon and watching with terrified eyes the swaying form of Aunt Becky Craft. On and on they raced; but several men on horses gave chase and they had not gone a great distance before one of the men succeeded in grasping a horn of one of the oxen, finally guiding the team into the rather smoother ground of the trail. At last they were brought under control and Aunt Becky, much shaken but otherwise uninjured, was able to get off her uncomfortable perch.

"How on airth did yer come thar?" queried her rescuer.

"Why, yer see I was walkin,' and when the critters began to run, I thought mebbe they smelled Injuns, and so I tried to git in the wagon; but the pesky things run so fast I couldn't quite make it. Was there any Injuns, or what was they runnin' fer?"

"Injuns? Nary a redskin! What the critters want is water and I s'pose they smelled it and felt like makin' a beeline for it. We're goin' to camp over beyond them bushes."

"Water! Huh!" said Aunt Becky. "If there's enough when we git thar, I'd just like to souse 'em in it, till they 'most drown."

"Say, Aunt Becky," said the grinning small boy, who had begun to look ruddy again under his freckles, "why didn't yer sing 'Home, Sweet Home,' or 'I'm Travelin' over Jordan' while yer was a-ridin'?"

"Let me git ahold of yer and yer'll wish yer was to hum," snapped the ruffled woman. "S'pose yer think 'tain't enough that yer most killt me, 'cause yer can't keep the steers in the trail, but yer must laugh about it afterward. Get out of here! I'll drive myself, before I see yer doin' it agin."

Day succeeded day and slowly the train moved onward towards the far Western place they all hoped to call home. The weather was variable; sometimes brilliant sunshine for days at a time, then a storm, often with thunder and lightning. The number of sick increased from day to day, and many were the sad or foreboding hearts. But sick or well, on they pressed with a persistency that challenges admiration.

The active children throve and grew strong under the bracing air of the Great Plains, and with the exercise they were obliged to take, they nearly all developed a physical hardiness that stood them in good stead later in their journey. It is true that clothes became faded by the sun and tattered by the constant wear, but if bodies are strong and minds clear, that matters little in the wilderness.

One day Tilda was looking out of the wagon, wishing the time would come faster when she, too, could go skipping along with the children, heedless of everything but the joy of being able to use her limbs in free motion as the rest did.

"I wish I had some of them flowers," she remarked wistfully, indicating some dusty, straggly ones, belated in their blooming. For a while the prairies had been fairly starred with beauty in May and June; now in late July, the beauty of spring had given way to the dryness of midsummer.

"If you'll see to Baby, I'll get you some flowers, though they're not very pretty," said Sis, as she crawled to the front of the wagon and poised for her customary leap.

"Better be careful how you jump, or you'll get hurt one of these times," called Mr. Sager who was walking beside the oxen. He caught sight of her as she was poising and called the warning that often occurred to him as the active youngsters jumped in and out.

Sis gave a gay little laugh and thought to herself, "I'll get out the way I've seen Mother do." So she sat down on the tongue and then attempted to step to the ground; but she had not remembered that she was not as tall as her mother and where

She fell directly in front of the wheel.

the latter could step firmly to the ground, then quickly in front of the wheel, she could not. Not reaching the ground as she had expected to, she was thrown off her balance and she fell directly in front of the wheel. Her father shouted a frantic "Whoa!" but this seemed to excite the oxen and they pressed on faster and the great wheel went directly over the prostrate form.

"My poor little child," cried Mr. Sager, as he

lifted the limp form. Sis had promptly fainted. When she came to, she looked up in bewilderment and seemed surprised to see her father looking so white and disturbed; and Mr. Caples was there, too, and she noticed there was blood on the latter's face.

"I guess I'm all right," she said weakly, making a move to get up, but a sharp numbing pain in one leg, made her lie down with a groan. "What is it, Pa?" she whispered with white lips.

Mr. Sager made no reply, but tried to straighten one limb that was lying crooked. This brought a pain so intense that poor Sis screamed and moaned convulsively. Mr. Caples in the meantime was wiping blood from her face which was bruised and scratched.

"I'm afraid her leg is broke," said her father, after an examination. "Whatever will we do, Mother?"

"Oh, I'm sure I don't know, I don't know!" said the distracted mother. "I suppose we must do what we can; but, if there was only a doctor with us! If we put on the splints ourselves, it might be the leg would always be crooked."

"I'll ride back and bring the Dutch doctor from the train behind, if you like, Mrs. Sager," said a sympathizing bystander. "I'm sure they're not far back, for we lost a day when we stopped to smoke that buffalo meat, and they wasn't far away before that. I was sure I saw the dust risin' from their train when we were on top of that butte back aways."

"If you only would," assented Mrs. Sager. "We'll keep bathing it in cold water if our supply only holds out. That'll keep the swelling down some till the doctor comes."

She hardly had the words out of her mouth before the messenger was off in the direction of the train behind. Sis moaned and cried though she very bravely tried to keep the tears back. A pallet was placed on the ground of the prairie and she was put in as comfortable a position as possible. A bandage was put on rather tightly and this was kept wet with cold water from the water bucket.

"Oh, Pa, I wish I hadn't been so foolish—but I always did it all right before," said Sis as her father stooped over her. "Will I have to be lame always?"

"I hope not, if we can git this doctor to set it, and I've no doubt he'll come," said her father. "You try to git a leetle nap now and it won't be long mebbe, before he'll git here."

Sis turned her head from side to side restlessly and the pitiful droop of the white, drawn mouth was heart-rending to her mother, but Baby was fretful and Louisa slightly ailing, with a degree of fever that worried Mrs. Sager. So her time had to be divided between the wagon and the child by the roadside.

## Chapter 6

# A Lonely Grave

**Sis looked up from her troubled stupor into a rotund, pleasant face bending over her.**

A CH! SO! I'll try not to hurt thee, *Liebchen. Ach!* Now quiet *dein* leetle heart. Vat for didst thou try to fly? Vell, *wenn die Vögel* fly, dey fly because wings hast they. But *haben Sie* wings? *Nein!* Den fly you shouldst not! *Nicht wahr?*"

These words, spoken in a hearty, sympathetic tone of voice, roused Sis from her troubled stupor of suffering and she looked up into a rotund, pleasant face bending over her. Blue eyes, brown hair, a straight nose, firm but tenderly shaped mouth, now nearly hidden by a growth of mustache and beard of several months' standing; these were the characteristics of Dr. Theopolis Dagin, who had just appeared, riding up hastily and throwing himself from his sweating horse. He knelt beside the pallet upon which the suffering child lay and with practiced hand was examining the injured limb.

"It is *gut* that you bandaged and kept the cold water on, *sehr gut.* It makes for to help. *Aber, ja!* the poor leg is sure broke." He looked up at Mrs. Sager, who, pale and shaken, had worked over her little daughter with a sad heart. With one little lame child on their hands, how could they ever stand it to have two? And this one so comforting and helpful as she had always been. The journey was growing harder and more uncertain every day, and great sadness filled the patient heart of this pioneer mother.

The setting of the limb was a bad time for poor Sis; but at last the splints were in place, and she was lying on the old feather bed in the wagon, a place she was to occupy for many weary days thereafter.

"I ride me *mit* you for an hour; den go I back to mine own place in *der* train pehindt. *Da* ist sick ones dere *auch, und den* must I see."

Then after an hour, when Sis was lying exhausted and quiet, "*Ach*, yes, she will do *gut* now; never fear you, Mrs. Sager. Now must I go the odder train but come I py the tomorrow. *Sie werden gut schlaffen—ach!* I mean she sleep *gut* dis night, if she take one more powder I gif you."

That night the wagon train made Fort Laramie. At the time of the accident there had been some talk of the whole train returning to the beautiful grove on the bank of the Platte where they had rested at noon; but it was finally decided to keep on to the fort, which they reached late. Leaving there the next morning, they struggled on over roads none too good. Sis had passed a fairly comfortable night, and when Dr. Dagin overtook them the next day, he pronounced his patient doing fairly well. The jolting of the wagon had proved so dangerous to the safety of the broken limb that Mr. Sager had made a long, narrow box for it to rest in. This prevented any bend that might disarrange the splints and so retard recovery.

It was hard to keep the children quiet, but Tilda amused herself with building air castles. "Do you know what I want to do when we get to Oregon, Ma?" she questioned. "I just want to play out of doors all day, 'cause I hate this old wagon so, and I think, if Pa'll let me, I'll have some little chickens all my own. May I, do you s'pose?"

"Indeed you may," said Mrs. Sager, glad to promise anything reasonable to make the way seem shorter for little lame Tilda. "I'm sure there'll be lots of chickens in Oregon for you to have."

A day or two after this, the doctor found that he had more than one patient on his hands. Sickness had become very prevalent. John, Frank, and Mr. Sager seemed to have a slight touch of the fever. So he very kindly agreed to stay with them for a few days, that he might the more easily watch their cases. He attempted to drive and thus relieve them of a part of their work, but he proved very unaccustomed to driving oxen, and many times a day Mr. Sager or the boys had to leave their beds in the wagon to help over rough and dangerous places. The boys improved, but the fever that had stricken the father seemed to increase from day to day. It finally became so bad that he could give very little help and most of the day he spent helpless in the slow lurching wagon. How welcome was the stopping time, when the tent could be pitched and he could drag himself out and throw himself upon the bedding in the tent.

Gradually a slight improvement came, and everything seemed more hopeful. Sis steadily improved, which made the whole family happy. John and Frank, recovering rapidly, stood by their tasks with a manful spirit, but try as they would to shake it off, the fever lodged in their bones, as they expressed it, leaving them weak and disinclined to much exertion.

The supply of game was much curtailed by this sickness and the provision supply began to be a serious problem. It was a source of great worry to Mr. Sager, who, now that he felt a little better, chafed and fretted as he saw the other men start off to hunt as he was wont to do. Not many days of his convalescence had passed when he called hurriedly for his gun as he sighted some buffalo and off he went, in spite of the protests of his wife. An hour later he returned, hot and tired, and threw himself on his bed in the wagon, seemingly very near the point of exhaustion. Mrs. Sager said nothing, but her anxiety grew.

That afternoon the fever again made itself evident and he was compelled to keep to his bed. In the morning he appeared alarmingly ill, but still the train moved on through dust and heat. He moaned and groaned occasionally as he roused from his stupor and in reply to his wife's questioning would say, "What *will* become of you all if I should die?

The man was very ill.

What can you do without me?" repeating this over and over again.

"But we don't expect you to die, Henry," his half-distracted wife would reply, striving to quiet her own fears as well as his, by hopeful words. But in spite of these words, a numbing, paralyzing fear was gripping her heart. Yes, what could she, a frail woman do, if he, the stalwart, buoyant husband, were to die here in the wilderness? By every art she had learned in many a sickroom, she fought the grim specter, and she was helped in every way by the doctor and many of the camping friends. It seemed a hopeless fight, however, and day by day he grew weaker.

Poor, helpless Sis, shut up under the same canvas cover, suffered torments of fear when the raging fever made her father's eyes staring and glassy, so unlike the usual, steady, quiet gleam she was accustomed to see; but when the fever quieted momentarily and he lay so still and helpless, another feeling quite new to the child's heart, took possession of it. A feeling that she must forget that she ever had an ache and that she must gain fast, so that she might help her mother more; a brooding, mothering feeling that made her conceal the terror she felt, whenever she was alone in the wagon with the sufferer. Every night he insisted on being removed to the tent, as the change seemed to relieve him.

In one of his lucid intervals, he requested that Captain Shaw come to see him and asked him to promise to help his family to their journey's end and place them in the care of Dr. Marcus Whitman, the missionary in far-off Oregon. He seemed to take much comfort in the thought that under the protection of this kind-hearted, helpful man, they would be able to make a start in the new country.

"Surely I'll stand by them, Sager. If we succeed

in getting to the Mission, your family shall, too. I give you my word," said Captain Shaw. "But don't give up. Take heart and try to live for the sake of those you love."

"I'm tryin' my best but I feel that I shan't pull through. No one knows what I suffer in my mind," he exclaimed, the tears running down his thin face. "The pain and sickness is nothing compared to it.

Kind hands drew the grieving widow and children gently away.

But I'll trust your word. You've bin a good friend an' I know you always will be to Naomi and the little ones. God bless ye!"

He also earnestly advised his wife to be guided by Dr. Whitman's experience. "Stay as near the Mission as you can. The good doctor has a kind heart, I feel sure, and what he knows of the country and people will be a great help to you."

Green River was reached at last and camp made upon its banks. But the sick man was very low, and after one more night of suffering, he died in the early dawn. Helpless, bereft of the one person in the whole world to whom she could turn with confidence, weak in body with the strain and overwork of the last few days, Naomi Sager felt the world grow unsteady and dim. She had received a blow from which she could not recover, no matter how bravely she might try to go on with the burden of living for the sake of her children.

A pleasant spot near the river was chosen and the men made a rude coffin by splitting and scooping out the two halves of a log. There on the bank of the river, with his heartbroken widow, his grieving children, and sympathizing friends standing by, all that was earthly of Henry Sager was lowered into the ground. Then silently, without the usual chatter, teams were hitched up, and on, ever on to the West, crept the slowly moving train.

# Chapter 7

# *The Seven Orphans*

MRS. SAGER, forced to turn aside from her sorrow for the practical demands of the journey, decided that the German doctor was hardly skillful enough as a driver longer to manage the oxen, so she hired a young man to take his place and urge the plodding beasts toilsomely westward.

John, with streaming eyes, had tenderly pressed his mother's hand and said comfortingly as they turned away from the grave, "I'm pretty big, Mother, and though I can't take *his* place, I'll do the best I can to take care of you all."

"I know you will do everything a boy of your age can do, my son; and Frank, too, is just as willing. You're the oldest though, John, and I must look to you more than to anyone else, to have a constant care for the younger ones. We will keep together, whatever comes. Remember that, John, you children must keep together."

A few days passed—days of journeying that brought with them no change in the heat and dust; but each succeeding night became cooler than the one before. They were struggling through the mountains and the way was exceedingly difficult. One morning when Aunt Sally Shaw stepped from her own wagon over to the Sagers' which stood near, she was greeted with pale, distressed faces.

"Mother is sick," said Sis, and the tears welled

up and ran down her face, which had not been washed that morning.

"You don't say!" exclaimed Aunt Sally. "Dear me, now don't be frightened, Sis. We'll all do all we can to help you. I'll go and find someone to look after the baby and then I'll come back and help the boys get breakfast."

So this kindly woman started on her errand and it was not many minutes before she was back with two or three other women. One took the baby, another bathed Mrs. Sager's flushed, drawn face, and Aunt Sally superintended breakfast.

"How're yer goin' to git yer own breakfast if you stay here to fix ours, Aunt Sally?" questioned Frank.

"Now don't yer trouble over that, my boy! If those big, strappin' men in my family can't git their own breakfast on a pinch, they can jest go hungry. It's a good idee to let 'em find out once in a while what a mother's good fer."

"Do you think Mother is awful sick?" asked John in a voice that would quaver in spite of himself. He had just come up to the campfire from the place where the oxen were feeding.

"Well, it ain't easy to say," said Aunt Sally cautiously. "She seems to have quite a fever, but I'm hopin' she'll be better in a day or two. Try to help all yer can and remember that Uncle Billy and Aunt Sally will do all they can fer you all," said the good woman, laying her kindly hand on the boy's shoulder. "We promised your father we'd look after yer and while we have a crust of bread, yer shall have part."

This was no promise lightly made and in the dreary weeks to come, it was literally fulfilled. A day came when the last loaf was divided between the Shaw and Sager families.

"I know you're always kind," replied John. "But if anything should—happen——" His voice trailed off into expressive silence.

"Eat yer breakfast now and try not to worry," responded the practical woman. "Mis' Gilliam has finished bathin' yer mother, and I'll give her this gruel. Can you boys pack up things? It won't be long before we have to move on. It's too bad the dust and heat are so bad; but we jest can't lose any more time and on we must go, sick or well."

Later in the day, the young man driving the Sager oxen suggested that John take his place for a short time and he would go hunting, if Mrs. Sager would permit him to take her husband's gun. She was reluctant to let him have it, but remembering how necessary game was to their diminishing larder, finally gave her consent. Off he went, and that was the last they saw of him. Long afterwards they found that he was in love with a young girl in the train ahead, and that he took this opportunity to overtake the other train and travel with it. They found the gun awaiting them at Dr. Whitman's Mission, where the young man had left it for them.

Off he went, and that was the last they saw
of him.

So John and Frank, with Dr. Dagin's help,
had to assume duties for which neither of the boys
had years or experience. Still, they did very well,
and the days crept on, but with little or no improvement in their mother's condition.

One day as they were on the top of a little hill
that gave them an excellent view, Tilda, wearied
with the confinement of the wagon, pointed out of
the open side, for the canvas had been thrown back

to admit more air, and said, "Mother, is Oregon over there?"

"Yes," said Mrs. Sager faintly and wearily, "Oregon is over there."

Tilda pulled herself up to a standing position, holding on to one of the slats, and looked long and earnestly towards the west. "But I don't see any chickens there, Mother," she said, turning a disappointed face to the other side of the wagon where her mother lay.

"But I don't see any chickens there, Mother."

Even in her distress, this brought a faint smile to the worn face. "You'll see them fast enough once we get there," said the mother.

"But when will we get there?"

"God alone knows that," replied the sad woman.

When they approached Fort Hall, Mrs. Sager sent the boys on ahead to the fort, where they were able to buy a little white sugar to sweeten her gruel and tea, for their supply was exhausted. Here she had intended to exchange her oxen and wagon for horses and continue on horseback to Dr. Whitman's station, hoping to winter there; but she was too ill to think of making any change. To give her some small degree of comfort, a sheet was hung over the front opening of the wagon in order to exclude the dust; but that resulted in even more stifling air within the wagon. This was the only thing possible to be done for her while the wagon was moving, and it seemed little enough to those who would so gladly have done more.

As camp was made that night near the fort, the women who came to bathe and assist her discovered that the feeble life was almost gone.

"Come quick!" called one who had knelt beside her to bathe the pale face. "Oh, Aunt Sally, I do believe she's gone a'ready."

"No," said Aunt Sally, "there's still a flutter of the pulse. The bathing may bring her to." And Aunt Sally applied more wet cloths to the patient.

But the cool water did not revive her and the hardly perceptible breath came fainter and fainter, finally ceasing altogether. Just at that moment, Frank came up to the spot and climbing on the wheel, said, "How's Mother?" The pitying women could not answer him but silently pointed to the still face.

The poor boy gave one long, heartbroken look and

then, with a long drawn-out "Oh!" fell to the ground unconscious.

The children, completely dazed and overcome by this new calamity, were taken in charge by pitying friends. The tent was hastily put up and the corpse removed to it for the night.

When morning came, a grave was dug by the roadside and the bottom covered with willow brush. The older children stood by in numb sorrow and saw the form of their dear mother carefully sewed in the sheet and lowered to its last resting place, saw more willow brush placed over it, and heard the clods of earth fall.

John turned to his brother and said haltingly, "Mother said for us to always stay together. You and I will have to make a home for the girls. We'll try to get to Dr. Whitman's Mission and maybe by that time we'll see how we're goin' to do it."

"Nefer you worry—you mine childer now," said the German doctor. "I could not save your mother's life, though hard did I try, but I can and will of you take care. I nefer leafe you more, but take you to dis *gut* Dr. Whitman. Dere stay you, an' den take I up de land, *und* a home for us all togedder make. Dat *ist ein gut* plan, *nicht wahr?*" he asked of Aunt Sally who stood near.

"It shows that you have one of the kindest hearts in the world!" rejoined Aunt Sally emphatically. "But I think you'll need lots of help, an' you must depend on all the rest of us to do all we're able.

There is not one in the train but what's anxious to do all they can. I am goin' to have their wagon always next to ours, so I'll be handy to show the girls how to do things."

So it was decided that the doctor was to stay with the children and in a way, make them "mine childer"; but Aunt Sally and Uncle Billy Shaw kept constant supervision, and most of the cooking was done by the compassionate women, who, regardless of their own hard work to provide suitable food for their families, had ever a thought for the fatherless and motherless children. The baby had been taken by kind Mrs. Eads and thus one responsibility was lifted off John's shoulders, who seemed to feel the burden of all they said or did.

The kindly doctor who so unselfishly came to the aid of the bereft Sager children was the son of a college professor in Germany. He had studied medicine, and after graduating, was happily married. In a terrible carriage accident his young wife was killed. He was soon given a government position as doctor on an emigrant ship, which he gladly accepted, thinking that it might help to distract him from his ever-present grief. Reaching the United States, the lure of the Far West took hold of him, and he resolved to explore this practically unknown part of America. Thus it was that he came so opportunely upon the troubles and sufferings of the Sager family.

The children rapidly accustomed themselves to

the changed circumstances. Like hardy plants which adapt themselves to change of soil, they soon grew accustomed to looking after themselves in large measure.

Their stock showed very plainly that the heavy wagon was daily becoming a burden too great for their strength, and at last Captain Shaw said to John and the doctor, "I believe it would be far better to stop for a day or two and make your wagon into a two-wheeled cart. Your critters is goin' to give out, I'm afraid, an' we've jest got to get this family to the Mission whether we get anywhere ourselves or not."

"But what will we do with the things?" objected John, who felt that the home belongings were very precious indeed.

"Why, we'll jest have to take the most needful of your clothing, bedding, and eatables. The rest I'll sell at auction if I can. You'll be glad to have some money when you reach Oregon. What we can't take or sell we'll have to leave. It's better so, my boy, than to try to hang to everything goin' through the Blue Mountains. The days will soon be gettin' shorter and it is your first duty to see to gettin' these little girls where they will be looked after better than we can do it."

Sis was still quite helpless, though Tilda had gained very much in the five months she had lived in the open. Their provisions, too, were so short that it was a great worry to Captain Shaw and the doctor. There was still bacon and some peas and beans, but the meal and flour were about gone. Fresh meat they had whenever the hunters were lucky enough to get any, for everyone shared generously with them.

Dr. Dagin approved the plan of making the wagon smaller; therefore, a halt of two days was ordered and the lumbering oxcart transformed into a two-wheeled affair which was much easier for the tired oxen to draw. The auction resulted in the disposal of a few of the household goods; but most people had about all they felt they could handle, and did not dare burden themselves with any more. Most of them, Captain Shaw included, were bent on getting into the Willamette Valley before winter. So when, on the morning of the third day, the train moved forward again, the children took a last look at many precious household things left lying by the roadside.

Tears welled up in John's eyes as he trudged on patiently beside the oxen. Oh, if they had never started on this awful journey! If they had only been content to remain in Missouri and endure malaria, rather than to come to such a pass! He looked dimly into the blue of the sky, a sky that appeared needlessly and frivolously cheerful, as it seemed to his heavy heart, and he wondered what the future might bring.

Tears welled up in John's eyes as he trudged on patiently beside
the oxen.

# Chapter 8

# Over the Blue Mountains

DOWN from the mountains swept a chill that made itself felt after the sun was gone. There was not so much room now in the wagon and the doctor and the boys slept on the ground. Toughened as the children had become by months of outdoor life, sleeping on the ground was not a serious hardship. Fear of Indians had grown less and less, and the solid formation of the camp for the night was seldom followed now, though of course the wagons were near each other. The strain, worry, and toil of the long journey had so far reduced the strength of many that when night came they were glad to throw themselves down almost anywhere, to secure what rest they could before the early drumbeat called upon them to endure the wearing, terrible march of the morrow, with its inevitable dust and discomfort.

"What's that noise, I'd like to know?" said Aunt Sally Shaw, sleepily raising her nightcapped head from its hard pillow one dark night. She shivered a little in the chill air, as she sat upright to listen better; for Aunt Sally always seemed to have a thought, sleeping or waking, for anything that might go amiss with the people under her husband's charge, and especially with the Sager family.

"Wake up," she continued, shaking Uncle Billy, who was sleeping the heavy sleep of a tired man, by

her side. "Wake up, can't ye? Seems to me, I hear
a child cryin' somewhere near."

Captain Shaw turned over with a yawn. "Sounds
to me like a coyote," he said drowsily. "The children usually sleep too well to be trottin' around
yellin' out in the open, in the middle of sech a cold
night as this."

"I was afraid it might be something the matter
with the Sager family," said his wife anxiously.

"Well, don't worry, old woman—they're all
right. Better go to sleep," said the Captain with
another yawn.

But his wife continued sitting up, listening intently to the sound that began after a short interval
of silence. It came in pitiful gasps and Aunt Sally
could hear it more plainly now.

"It *is* some child and you must get right up and
see about it!" and she gave her husband such a
shake that sleep was effectively banished from his
eyes.

Wide awake now, the Captain dressed and
sprang out of his wagon, hastily lighting his lantern, for the night was pitch dark. He hurried in
the direction of the sound. Some distance from the
wagons it appeared to be and seemed receding
slowly. Every now and then it would stop momentarily, as though the child had tripped and fallen
over some obstruction, then gathered itself to its
feet, to resume its cry with increased force. Such
a note of helplessness and terror was in that cry

**Just then the dim light of his lantern brought to his eyes the
terrified face of a little girl.**

that the Captain's heart beat fast with sympathy as he hurried forward.

"*Must* be one o' them Sager children," he thought. "Surely no youngster with a father or mother to tend to 'em would wander off like this. Land, but I'll be thankful if I ever get 'em all in a safe place!"

Just then the dim light of his lantern brought to his eyes the terrified face of a little girl, who stood near, shivering with cold and fright, the unwiped tears flowing over cheeks browned by tan and the dust and grime of travel.

Before he could speak, she gave one cry of happy relief and flung herself upon him, crying, "Oh, Cap'n Shaw, I fought I got lost. But you'll find me, won't you?"

"I should say I have found you already! But how on earth did you come here, I'd like to know?" said the Captain, giving an inward blessing for Aunt Sally's keen ears.

"I just s'pose I got cold a-sleepin' and mebbe went a-walkin' to get warm; but I was so drefful sleepy, I s'pect I don't know much about it," she answered, cuddling down on his broad shoulder, as the good Captain lifted her in his arms.

"Here, you boys! Wake up and take care of this baby, can't you?" said the Captain a few minutes later, stirring John and the doctor vigorously with his foot.

They sat up, looking much bewildered, the doctor

blinking like a disturbed owl, as the rays of the lantern flashed into his eyes.

"Heard her cryin' away out on the prairie where she'd wandered in her sleep," continued Captain Shaw. "Now, let her lie down between you and then see if you can keep track of her. S'pose she was cold and that made her get up and crawl out o' the wagon." Little Louisa, deposited between her brother and the doctor, was off in a deep sleep of exhaustion and content before the Captain's lantern rays were extinguished at his wagon near by.

Louisa was none the worse next morning for her startling experience; but the fright she gave them all made her looked after sharply for a few days at least. The little girls who had been sleeping with her in the wagon had not wakened as she left them and knew nothing of the occurrence until the next day.

The boys and the doctor found that packing a two-wheeled cart was a somewhat ticklish business. It required nicety of judgment to adjust everything so that it balanced well, and many were the incidents that gave amusement to their friends and severe tests of patience to themselves. Things always seemed to go wrong when they were late and in a hurry.

One morning, soon after Louisa's episode, the doctor climbed into the cart to stow away things for the day. They were behind with their preparations and he was trying to hurry. One or both of the boys were supposed to hold the tongue down, so the cart would not "end up," but this particular day a washtub filled with fresh-killed beef was accidently placed a little beyond the center of gravity, and the doctor in moving around shoved it a little more.

The cart began to tip and the doctor called excitedly, "Chon! Chon! get you holt mit de tongue, *so schnell* as you can! Frank! Chon! *Schnell!* See you not—*ach, donnerblitzen!* Dem boys *sind* nefer *wo* they shouldst be!" Then his remarks were brought to an abrupt close, as barrel, bedding, dishes, and everything else movable shot toward the back as the rear end of the wagon came to the earth with a thud. The doctor clung to the front end high in the air, for an instant, and then, clawing frantically but fruitlessly at the bare boards of bottom and sides, ignominiously slid down the incline and landed sputtering among the utter confusion of household goods below.

The boys who had been picking up the little things of the camp, and had not been near enough to prevent the accident, were convulsed with laughter. John tried weakly to spring up and catch the tongue of the wagon which was pointing skyward, but doubled up as he was, his fingers failed to grasp it and before trying again, he had to sit down on the ground and laugh until the tears ran down his cheeks. Frank was no better off and he, too, shouted and laughed. He, like the rest of the children, was much attached to their eccentric helper; but being a boy, he did love to play jokes; and when he noticed the long legs and arms working their way somewhere near the surface of the debris, it took but an instant to dexterously tip some of the bundles onto, instead of away from, the struggling hero, thereby retarding the moment of his release.

Then he quickly slipped to the front of the wagon and, by the time Dr. Dagin had found his feet, was busily engaged with John in holding down the tongue. After that for a while, there was no time between the work of restoring order and the numerous vigorous German invectives, to laugh; but for many a day to come, there were merry references to this mishap that served to keep the memory of it alive. But another accident made this mishap of small importance.

"Just you girls keep further away from that there fire, or you'll wish you had," was the anxious warning often repeated by one or the other of the two brothers to the little girls.

"Oo-o-o-o!" shivered Sis one morning, as she hobbled out to the fire. "I've found out at last where these mountains got their name. It's so cold here that everybody feels blue. That's why they're called the Blue Mountains." Sis had been provided with some impromptu crutches and with their aid managed to get about.

The fire was almost the only comfort they had

nowadays. The mornings were sharp and frosty, or cold and damp with threatened rain. Before starting off for the daily struggle, or after the weary journey of that day was done, it was good to get close to the blaze and "toast" and relax weary limbs.

"I wish you would get away a little, so I could get to the fire to boil this coffee," said Frank a little impatiently to Elizabeth, who was trying to warm herself. The wind came down raw and cold and her cotton dress was none too warm.

"Just go 'long and find something else to do and I'll see to the coffee," answered Elizabeth in the same impatient tone.

They still had some coffee left, which was more than some of their neighbors had. Only the night before, one of their friends had come to their wagon, saying to Sis, "Could you manage to spare me a little coffee? We're entirely out and wife is sick and craves some so. I've brought this to pay for it," and he held out a rosary. Sis immediately gave this traveling neighbor part of her store, and the rosary became an object of interest to the Sager children.

"My, ain't it good to get warm!" said Elizabeth, poking the embers around the coffeepot and then turning her back to the fire, so that the comforting heat might warm both sides.

The wind came in a sudden gust and swept a fold of the thin cotton dress Elizabeth wore near the flame. A second later, Sis, Matilda, and Louisa were horrified to see their sister's clothes ablaze. Their terrified screams brought Frank on a run from a short distance away, where he had been looking for more wood; but Dr. Dagin had also heard the first note of alarm and reached the spot before Frank could.

Regardless of his own danger, he seized the girl and smothered the flames by unceremoniously rolling her over and over upon the ground.

It was all over in a moment, but it left Elizabeth weak and frightened, though unhurt. As for the brave, self-forgetful doctor, the skin was burned almost entirely from both hands.

The children were too overcome to venture a word of reproof to the careless sister and Dr. Dagin was too occupied with his own sufferings to do more than mutter, "Dat Lisbet! Dat Lisbet! She one big bunch of mischief, dat Lisbet *ist. Aber* I am *sehr* glad—*O mein Gott*, I gif Thee thanks, that she not burned *ist*. It is *gut* that I, a man, go mitout some of mine skin and she, *eines kleines Mädchen*, save hers whole. What could I have said to Thee, *lieber Vater im Himmel*, hadst she been cooked? Ach! but she all de same one mischief, dat Lisbet."

It was some days before the doctor's hands had healed enough to permit him to do much work. And to add to his miseries, he became quite ill with dysentery caused by the almost constant diet of meat. This trouble had become very prevalent throughout the entire train.

The flour of the whole company had given out, and meat three times a day was the rule. The Shaws had, some time before this, baked their last loaf of bread and, true to their promise of looking after the Sager family, had divided it with them. Fortunately, game could be had, and there was still stock enough along to kill an occasional "beef critter." The Sager cows had been taken by the Eads when Mrs. Eads had taken the baby to care for; but the children were sent for, now and then, and given a drink of milk. When the doctor became very weak and ill, with even his happy, hopeful courage getting low, he, too, was given some milk. In after years he remarked many times that that milk saved his life.

The frying pan, freely used in the beginning of the trip, had given way, in the Sager family at least, to the more primitive method of cooking meat on sticks before the blaze. This, of course, was during the hurry of the breakfast and noon hour. When camp was made for the night, there was then time to swing the big six-gallon kettle over the fire and prepare an appetizing stew. As long as the flour lasted, John or the doctor always made dumplings.

"Well, anyway," said Sis to John one day, "I shall stop eating when we get where one fellow was!"

"Where was that?" inquired her brother.

"Why, I saw him cuttin' off slices of raw meat and eatin' it down as if it was good. I asked him if he didn't cook his meat, and he said, no, he hadn't any time to get wood, or to cook it if he had the wood; that it was just as good that way, anyhow. It made me sick to see him and I just came back quick to our own wagon, when he offered to give me some."

"The pass some of us have come to is pretty bad, I reckon," said John soberly. "We will do the best we can, but our best isn't very good sometimes."

The two-wheeled cart was much easier to get over the ground than the heavier four-wheeled wagons, and one morning John warned Frank not to get too far ahead, when it was the turn of the Sager cart to lead the weary procession. John was busy filling the powder horn with the last of the powder. Not that he intended to take it with him, for he was to drive cattle all that day and there would be no chance for him to go hunting; but he was thinking that by tomorrow he might have a chance and he would have everything in readiness.

The bleak wind whistled and sang through the sparse pines and the sagebrush that grew in endless profusion on the never-ending way. It goaded the tired oxen to quicker movements than usual, and, in spite of John's caution, the Sagers' cart soon outdistanced the rest of the train and was far in advance.

As they reached one eminence and halted the

panting oxen to allow them to rest a bit, they looked
back and saw the straggling procession toiling on
several miles behind. The sky was leaden, with
no hint of comfort or hopefulness. The spirit of
discomfort seemed to settle over every living thing.
The children could not help seeing the pitiful,
dreary droop of horses, cattle, men, women, and
even the dogs. The latter trailed along beside their
masters with low-hung heads and tails, every move
indicating and emphasizing the terrible hardships
and discouraging toil of the trip. Even the tattered
canvas covers seemed more than usual to flaunt
their used-up condition to the bare world.

"It's so cold, let's go down into this holler and see
if the wind won't cut less down there," said Elizabeth, hopping uneasily from one bare foot to the
other, for the hundreds of miles of travel had
played havoc with the shoes so carefully made by
Mr. Sager before leaving Missouri, and for weeks
the entire family had been obliged to go without.
Sometimes it was fairly easy to do without shoes,
but the days of walking through prickly pear were
days of torture even to their hardened skins.

Frank and the doctor remained on the crest of
the hill with the oxen, but the little girls ran,
walked, and limped their several ways to the bottom and then ventured on a little farther, for they
had to keep moving, to keep even fairly warm. The
train was following, at a distance of from two to
five miles from its banks, the course of a winding

Walking through prickly pear was torture.

river; they were trying to come to the fording place.
Where the little girls were, an opening between the
rolling hills gave a view of this river and its opposite shore.

Their attention was suddenly called to a sound of
shouting, and looking across this river, they discovered, to their terror, a band of Indians shouting
and waving their hands at them. The frightened
little girls, out of sight and sound of all their
friends, made a frantic rush in the direction of the
hill, at the top of which were Frank and the doctor.

Not a word did they utter, for fear paralyzed their vocal cords; only a little sound, half groan, half sob, escaped them as they made all possible haste to rejoin their protectors. Elizabeth, active and vigorous, dragged little Hannah Louisa by the hand, because Tilda and Sis had all they could do to help themselves. Indeed, Sis in her terror, finding others were getting ahead of her, dropped her

Sis dropped her crutches and went up the hill on hands and knees.

crutches and went up the last half of the hill on hands and knees.

"Pooh!" said Frank, when they breathlessly told of their fright. "Why didn't you stop a minute to see if they acted ugly or not? See, there they go now," he added, as he walked a little way forward for a better view. "And they're goin' straight away from the river, too, so you didn't need to be so scared. Let's drive the team down the hill," he said to the doctor. "It's too cold to stand here any longer. We can build a fire and let the girls warm up a bit, before the others catch up."

"Won't the Indians come back?" objected Sis doubtfully.

"How are they goin' to cross the river? Couldn't you see how swift it is and don't you know we're two days at least from the fording place?" answered Frank.

"*Ich* tink they come not back, *Mädchen. Sie haben Freundschaft für uns.* Fear you not," observed Dr. Dagin, who, many times every day, lapsed into his mother tongue. Indeed, he had taught the children the German name for many things, as they traveled over the dreary miles. Thus they were as familiar with "*der Messer*" and "*die Tasse*" as with "knife" and "cup."

So Sis plucked up her courage and went down the hill with the rest, picking up the discarded crutches by the way. Once at the bottom, she found to her relief that the Indians were entirely out of sight.

Building the fire was not so easy that day. There had been rain, and every bit of wood was wet; and the slight mist effectively dampened the enthusiasm of the flicker that Frank at last succeeded in coaxing into being.

"No use tryin' to do things this way," he said impatiently. "I'll make the old thing burn, see if I don't!"

"How'll you do it, I'd like to know?" asked Tilda.

"There isn't a speck of dry wood anywhere around."

"You children run behind the wagon where you'll be safe, and I'll tend to the fire all right," answered Frank, going towards it from the wagon with the powder horn which John had filled that morning.

The children obediently ran behind the wagon, peeping around the ends, wondering what on earth their brother was about to do. The horn was neatly scraped and polished and its ends had been stopped with two plugs of wood; in the small end, out of which the powder was usually poured, was a very small one. The larger end was likewise fitted with a wooden plug, very tightly wedged in. This larger one was removed only when it was necessary to fill the horn. In the center of this was a short nail, to which was attached one end of the thong by means of which it was slung over the shoulder and under the arm in hunting; the other end of the string was tied around the small end of the horn.

Frank bent carefully over the fire which showed no sign of animation and poured a small portion of the precious powder from the small end of the horn onto the apparently extinguished pieces of charred wood.

The next instant a loud noise greeted the watching children, and brother Frank was seen to turn a somersault backward, then jump up and run frantically to a little creek that ran along the bot-

tom of the gully. The doctor came running up from
a little distance, where he had been hunting drier
wood, and the children rushed out from behind
the wagon.

After a short time Frank came back looking
very sheepish as well as peculiar. His face was
badly scorched, his eyebrows and lashes were entirely burned off and his hands had also suffered
seriously. "Are my eyes hurt?" he asked the doctor.
"I can stand the rest all right."

The doctor could not help smiling at his grit and
after an examination decided the eyes were not
seriously injured. He bound up the burns as best
he could, but he had no skill to restore the lost eyebrows and lashes, and it was long before they
started to grow again. Later, after they had
reached the Mission, the Indians gave Frank an
Indian name meaning "No Eyebrows."

The cause of his sudden somersault was the tre-
mendous impact of the large wooden plug, which
was blown out of the horn and gave him a blow in
the stomach. He learned a lesson that morning
that caused him to be exceedingly careful in the
use of powder the rest of his life.

After the rest of the train had overtaken them
and Frank had been scolded or laughed at, accord-
ing to the mood of his different neighbors, they all
moved on together and that night were forced to
make a dry camp. Their course had veered away
from the river, which they had caught glimpses of

earlier in the day. Probably the poor stock suffered much more than the people, for nearly every wagon had a little water stored away for use. The morning had opened threateningly, but the sky became clear by early afternoon, so there was no chance of rain which would have allowed them to catch some of the precious drops.

An early start was made next morning, for water must be found or all would perish. Fortunately, the scouts who left camp as soon as there was enough light to allow them to see a short distance ahead, had stumbled onto a small creek only a few miles away and they hastily returned to guide the train to the life-giving water.

After that, the days passed as had so many others. They were making fewer and fewer miles each day because of the exhausted condition of their cattle.

The next obstruction across their way was the Boise River which they had caught glimpses of so many times in the last few days. Frank drove the Sager wagon across and as the oxen had to swim a part of the way, it was not a very dry load that was driven up the western bank of the river into the tall rye grass that stood in sere and yellow ranks waving shoulder high. Other wagonloads were in a like condition, and there was nothing to do but to lay over and dry off; so camp was made and things hastily spread on bushes, trees, anywhere that would offer support.

The attention of some of the workers was diverted for a time, however, by the trials of one pioneer to get his carriage across the stream. He had insisted on bringing this heavy vehicle, because as he said, "No one knows how many years it will be before I can get one out there and I have it and I'm going to keep it." It had been troublesome before in getting across some of the streams, but this seemed worse than most, for it sank in the water, and all efforts to "hist" it seemed useless. The wheels were not removable and there seemed no way to get the thing out of the hole into which it had fallen.

The men tried again and again, but it still stuck. The Indians, in whose canoes the women and children had been ferried across, were vastly interested, and one made signs to the owner of the carriage that he thought he could raise it. Several things like handkerchiefs, beads, pieces of calico were offered him if he would undertake it, but he scornfully shook his head. No, he was already rich in such things, for had not his canoe been used to carry passengers across before and were not these articles the reward of such service?

"Well," said the owner, "if that won't suit, mebbe this will," and he pointed to his own weather-beaten shirt of checked homespun.

A delighted smile of acceptance came over his dusky face, and, throwing off the scanty clothing he was wearing, he soon swam out, tugged, pulled, and lifted, sometimes under the water, sometimes above, seemingly as much at home in the liquid element as on land. He finally succeeded in starting the reluctant vehicle towards the shore. Proudly did he later disport himself before his fellows, wearing the checkered reward of his labors! What was a half or three quarters of an hour in the chill, swift-running waters, when for days thereafter he might flaunt the glories of this new shirt "made paleface way" in the faces of his envious brother braves?

Meanwhile Elizabeth and Almira Eads, who had wandered from the train, came across a lone Indian fishing about a mile above the place where the others were beginning to cross the river. Evidently he was skillful, for a large pile of dried fish lay on the riverbank. He had piled them up two or three feet high, much as a rick of wood is piled, and when he saw the girls looking at them hungrily, gave Elizabeth a piece which she tried to eat. But smoked and without salt, it did not seem palatable to her and she had hard work to get even a portion of it down.

Almira pointed to the farther shore, then to the canoe lying near, then to themselves and finally to the swarthy red man.

He seemed to comprehend her wishes, after the motions had been repeated several times, and with a nod of assent, led the way down the bank to the canoe. The waters rushed by with a strong sweep, but the Indian's arms were accustomed and vigorous, and the canoe soon reached the opposite shore. Almira had only a soiled homespun handkerchief to give their ferryman, but this he took with evident satisfaction and then went placidly back across the stream to his fishing.

The girls walked on down the river to the place where camp was being made and as they neared the Eads wagon, Elizabeth noticed among the comforts, quilts, and garments which were hung out on the bushes to dry, several yards of white cloth.

"What's your ma goin' to do with all that white cloth, Almira?" she asked curiously.

"That? Oh, that's the cloth for her shroud," returned Almira. "You know she was in dreadful poor health before we started and she was afeard she might die afore she got to Oregon; in fact, everybody expected she would. So last winter, she spun and wove this cloth, so she would not have to be buried in a dress. But instead of growin' sicker, she's been gettin' better and better, till now she's perfectly well and I reckon won't need the cloth for years. You know lots of women did the same thing, only some made their shrouds afore they started. Ma didn't have time for anything but the weavin'."

Elizabeth thoughtfully fingered the soft folds of the cloth, which resembled fine cambric. Finally she said with a sigh and a troubled look in her eyes, "My mother didn't make a shroud for herself. Ain't it queer? And she was so well when she started. And she needed one, and your mother was so sick and got everything ready and now she don't need it. Things don't go straight always, do they?"

"They go just contrary to what we might expect sometimes, that's a fact. But it isn't always given us to think out clear what's best for us, Ma says," replied Almira. "How's the baby, Ma?" she questioned.

"The pore leetle thing is mighty weak and I don't reckon she'll last long, unless there's a change for the better right soon," said Mrs. Eads gravely. "Elizabeth, child, you'd better tell Sis to send me Baby's best dress if she can find it, for like as not it'll be needed soon and it must be washed up good."

Sis, who was helping John and the doctor dry some of their belongings, found the dress and took it over to Mrs. Eads. It was soft and white and had been made from a portion of Mrs. Sager's wedding dress. The older sister handled it with reverent touch and said wistfully as she put it in Mrs. Eads's hands, "I hope Baby will get better so you'll not need to use it. Of course if she needs it, she must have it; but I'd like to keep it always, 'cause it's all we have of Mother's weddin' dress."

"I'm doin' all I can for your little sister, my child, but she's awful sick and unless the good Lord works a miracle, I'm afraid she'll be called to jine your pa and ma up in Heaven. And if she should die, I know you'd want her laid away in this pretty white dress. It's little enough we can do for our dead,

out here on this terrible trip; but we must wash
and have it ready against a time of need."

Sis went to the wagon, took one look at the wan,
pinched face, and then returned to her work with
a heavy heart. Surely life was trouble upon trouble!

# Chapter 9

# *Waiilatpu—Land of Rye Grass*

IT TOOK time and patience to get down from the mountains to the rolling level of the valley. But finally it was accomplished without serious mishap, and the day seemed near at hand when the Sager family would have to leave the companions they had journeyed with so long. They were at last only twenty-five miles from Waiilatpu ("Land of Rye Grass"), Dr. Whitman's Mission.

Here, where the rest of the party would need to take another road to get to The Dalles, a halt was called; and the next day, October 15, Captain Shaw went on horseback to Dr. Whitman's to see if he could arrange with him to care for the orphan family. In the meantime, the children undertook to tidy themselves and their belongings as much as possible.

Thanks to Aunt Nancy Nichols who, with the utmost kindness of heart, had washed and mended faithfully for them, their clothes, though worn and faded, still held together. "But the tan and freckles and the scraggly hair!" thought Sis.

She scrubbed the younger ones faithfully, aided by the soft soap made by the mother in Missouri, a small portion of which still remained. Careless and unused to thorough bathing as they had become in the last sad months, the children found this an ordeal. But with determination that held out against dirt stains and rebellion, Sis held to her task until there was at least a slight improvement.

"You needn't think you're goin' to the Mission with *your* hair lookin' like that, Miss," said John to her, as she was resting after her labors. "Jest let me trim it up a bit for you."

Owing to her sickness and want of care, Sis had lost much of her hair, and sun, alkali dust, and wind had made what remained dry and ragged. Armed with some dull shears and a comb, John started in to play barber. So many tasks had been put upon his boyish shoulders that he assumed this with confidence as being easy. But the snarls were plentiful, and naturally tenderhearted as John was, it was painful to him to have his sister squirm and cry under his hand, so he began cutting out the snarls, which made the work easier, but hardly attractive.

"It looks kinder bobbery, but it's the best I can do," he remarked, as he stepped back to survey the job. "I can't seem to get it very even, but it will soon grow out, I reckon," he consoled. "You see some of the snarls were close to your head and the others weren't, and so someway I couldn't manage very well."

"Looks mighty like old Sal, who was always interferin' with the rest o' the cattle and gettin' a bunch of hair rubbed off her here and there," remarked Frank with brotherly frankness.

"I don't care how it looks, jest so I don't have to

So many tasks had been put upon his boyish shoulders that John
assumed this with confidence as being easy.

have my head pulled around any more," said Sis
with a sigh of relief. "Here come some Indians and
if they're wantin' to scalp me, I won't mind much,
after what I've been through."

But it was not scalps they were after. Instead,
they were extremely friendly and said with placid
gravity, "We Whitman Indians," meaning they
knew Dr. Whitman and were converts to his teaching. They were well supplied with potatoes, the
first the emigrants had seen for months and they
had also some camas bread with them. The Sager
family parted with an old tablecloth and secured
enough for one or two good meals.

The potatoes seemed like a royal banquet to the
vegetable-famished children; and the queer bread,
made by pounding the onionlike root of the camas
plant and then drying out before a fire the cakes
made from the pulp, was also a blessed change
from the monotonous meat diet.

Captain Shaw returned late in the evening and
after leaving his tired horse grazing with the rest
of the stock, went to his wagon. His wife was
bursting with eager questions.

"And did ye see the Whitmans, old man?" asked
Aunt Polly.

"Yes, I saw them and they are a mighty nice-
appearing couple, I can tell you. We can make no
mistake in leaving the children in their care, for the
Doctor is a fine man and Mrs. Whitman is not only
pretty as a picture, but she's a lady clear through.

They're the right sort of folks to do things in a new country, I can tell you."

"But are they goin' to take the children? That's what I'm most worried over," continued Aunt Sally.

"Well, they didn't want to at first, but I talked to 'em smart as I was able, and they finally said they would take the girls for the winter and if they was pleased with 'em, mebbe adopt them later. I don't see any way but for John and Frank to go along with the Dutch doctor and try and get some land. It'll most break the boys' hearts, but it was the best I could do this time; though I'm goin' back with the children tomorrow and mebbe I can make different arrangements."

John and Frank were indeed disturbed when they were told that they would probably have to be separated from their sisters; and it was a sad-hearted party that left the rest of the train the following morning, to journey on by themselves and find a home among strangers.

"But what can we do, I'd like to know?" said John mournfully. "Father and Mother both said that we were to go to Dr. Whitman's and maybe if we do as they wanted, it will come out all right."

Frank said with an ineffectual attempt to conceal a sob, "I don't see that there's much worth workin' for, if Father and Mother, and sisters are *all* gone and just us two left together. 'Tain't right, and I'd just as lief stay here as go on!" and he sat down forlornly on the ground with the air of one who has not an ounce of courage left.

"Nefer you mind, Frank, *mein* boy; you'll still haf me left to play your tricks on, and that will keep you some alife. *Ach*, yes! I'm like the big Irishman who had a very shmall wife *mit* a big tongue, what scold all de time. His friends said *mit* him 'Dennis, what for don't you gif her von big whippin' *und* mebbe she stop scold some of de time?' But de Irishman scrooge his dick shoulders *und* say, 'It don't hurt me none, but it do her mooch *gut*, so let her scold all she vill *und* enjoy life.'"

Frank could not help smiling at this, in spite of the tears standing in his eyes; for numberless were the tricks and jokes he had played on the doctor from day to day, during the last three months.

Mrs. Shaw took an affectionate though tearful leave of the little family. "Ye shouldn't go a step into the hands of strangers, if it was so we could keep ye all," she remarked more than once. "But we've our own way to make and in this strange, new country, too. You just remember, if you all can't stand it, let us know and we'll manage to help someway."

And as long as the cart was in sight, the tender-hearted woman watched, standing granite-like, until the blue haze of an Oregon October day hid her little friends from her sight. "The saddest sight I ever saw," she said in after years. "Them pore children goin' off, turnin' their faces back over their shoulders every minute or so, so wishful-like, and goin' to find a strange home among strangers!"

The baby had been left with the Eadses, as it was evidently near to death. The children had climbed up on the wagon wheel that morning, to take what they thought was their last look at the little wizened face. So sad and depressed were they, however, that they did not grieve unduly.

Captain Shaw went with them; but the weary cattle made such slow time that it was not until between ten and eleven of the following day that they came in sight of the Mission.

The house of the Whitmans was a comfortable-looking building, built somewhat in the shape of a huge T, and stood in an open, sunny spot. Though it faced the west, the front door was seldom used, nearly everyone approaching by the kitchen door, which opened to the north. A palisade went from the corner of the Indian room to the corner of the unfinished ell on its north side, and there was also one on the south side, extending from the corner of the parlor to the farther corner of the ell. These had been put there when the house was first built as a protection against possible hostilities on the part of the Indians, but they were removed within a few days after the children reached the Mission, all fear of the Indians having left the minds of the Whitmans. A field fence at a distance of some four hundred feet was on the north and east; the Walla Walla River was on the south; and on the west the

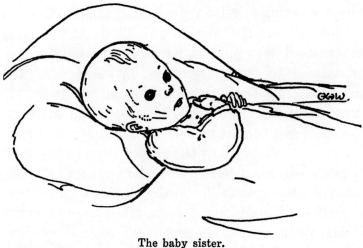

The baby sister.

field fence extended far enough to enclose large fields of grain.

Not far away, but just outside the field fence to the east, stood a large, square, story-and-a-half building of adobe (as was the Mission), and known as the mansion-house, a dwelling where emigrants were welcome to remain for a long or short time, as suited their needs and convenience. Some of those on their way to the Willamette Valley would tarry here for a time to rest their weary bodies, weakened by the terrible journey over the endless trails of mountains and prairie, and then, refreshed and encouraged with gifts from Dr. Whitman of food and of seed for future harvest, would take a fresh start and go forward to plant the tiny beginnings of new farms, villages, and towns.

The mansion-house was built by a man named

Gray, a young missionary who had come to Oregon with Whitman and Spalding in 1836. At this time it was used in summer as a granary, but given over in winter to the emigrants. It stood near the millpond, and the gristmill was not far away. It was about four hundred feet from the Mission, and between them was a small building used as a blacksmith shop. Near that, but a little to one side, was the corral, enclosed with slabs set up endwise. Between the gristmill and the Doctor's house was a good-sized, well-kept garden, while the cultivated fields of grain lay to the south and west. There was a large millpond just behind the mansion-house, water being brought to it from the river by an aqueduct. A large irrigation ditch from this mill-pond ran on the north side of the Whitman house, and numerous laterals from it ran over the farm, helping to produce the generous crops of vegetables and grains.

For weeks the children had talked of how they expected the Whitman Mission to look, and they had agreed that it would be much like Fort Hall, with disorderly looking buildings and armed men lounging about. So when they finally came to it they were much impressed with the neat buildings and with the air of thrift and orderliness over everything.

"And I s'pose Dr. Whitman will look so grave and good; but I don't reckon he will smile much, do you?" Tilda had said speculatively. "And Mis'

Whitman will prob'ly be kinder nice, too; but I don't know why, only I'm afraid she will be too busy to talk to us much."

"I don't s'pose they'll like me to play many jokes on them," said Frank, "but I can stand that, if they don't expect me to pray all the time."

As they neared the Mission, Captain Shaw pressed on ahead of the wagon. He was in the house, talking with Mrs. Whitman, when the little group of forlorn children drove up and halted.

The tired cattle had lain down the minute they had stopped, and Dr. Dagin, whip in hand, stood near the head of the first of the three yokes. An emotion too strong for words had seized the warm-hearted man, and his face, which had grown thin and old in the last weeks, was tense with the inward struggle he was making to preserve his wonted calm.

Captain Shaw came hastily out of the house and said, "Now, boys, find the girls' sunbonnets and help them out of the wagon." With moist eyes, the search for the bonnets began. They had been worn but little, if at all, for many days, and though the search was prolonged, but one or two could be found and they were not in good condition.

The girls by this time were on the ground, huddled barefooted and bareheaded by the side of the cart. John, in the front of the battered, travel-worn wagon home, had lost entire control of his feelings and was weeping bitterly, while Frank, with both arms resting on a wheel rim and head bowed on arms, sobbed aloud.

The little girls were too absorbed in watching the movements of a rather tall, serene-looking woman who had left the house and was coming toward them, to note acutely the distress of their brothers, though they alternately looked at them, then at the house, and then at the woman advancing—dreading they knew not what!

The tall woman was Mrs. Whitman. She was very sweet-looking; she seemed even beautiful to the four pairs of girlish eyes watching her. Her dress, plain but very neatly made, was of dark reddish calico, and she wore a gingham sunbonnet. This covered the profuse, silky auburn hair, but the children could see the steady gray eyes, the straight nose, and the firm line of mouth and chin, all bespeaking courage and resolution.

"How do you do, my little girls?" she said in a sweet voice, the kindliness of which was unmistakable, though it sent them scurrying behind the wagon, from which point of vantage they peeped out, like so many shy, wild birds, at this new friend.

Mrs. Whitman looked a bit surprised at this reception and, noticing the crying boys, said, "Why are you crying?" Then without waiting for them to reply, she said to herself, "No wonder they cry, poor boys." Seeing an Indian woman squatted near by on the ground, Mrs. Whitman began to address her in her own language, which so interested the

girls that they forgot their fright and came out of
their hiding place.

The boys put upon the ground the things they
were to leave for their sisters, and Mrs. Whitman
began to arrange them in an orderly way, talking
all the time to the Indian woman, who was an
interested observer of her work.

A little girl of seven came up, and shy looks were
exchanged between her and the new arrivals. The
little girl seemed to be very pretty and, to the Sager
children, very well dressed. The green dress and
white apron were simple enough, but so carefully
made and neatly put on, that they appeared like
fine apparel to the four ragged Sager girls. Later
they found that her name was Helen Meek, and that
she was a daughter of Joe Meek, the trapper, who
was then away to hunt furs.

Mrs. Whitman directed the boys to take the
things to the house and, taking little Louisa by the
hand, said, "Now we will go to the house, children."
Noticing how lame Sis was, she extended her other
hand to her, and with Tilda, Elizabeth, and Captain Shaw following the little party made its way
across the ditch and up to the house, the door of
which stood hospitably open. As they reached the
step, Captain Shaw asked, "Have you children of
your own, ma'am?"

A fleeting shadow came over the sweet face as
she answered, pointing to a small grave at the foot
of a hill not far off, "The only child I ever had sleeps

yonder. It is a great comfort to me that I can see her grave from our door."

She referred to the little daughter, "Little White Cayuse," as the Indians called her, who in 1839 was drowned while trying to get some drinking water from the river near by. The mother had been too busy with her duties for the welfare of the many who came to the Mission for help, to watch the little one closely all the time. One Sunday afternoon the child had taken her two tin cups and slipped away unnoticed. Later, when she was missed and search was made, the cups were found on the bank, and a faithful Indian friend, diving, came to the surface of the water, the dead child in his arms.

But the brave pioneer father and mother did not let their grief overwhelm them. They only redoubled their efforts to help others who needed what they so freely and cheerfully gave.

Going into the house, the Sager children found a little girl, seemingly about nine years old, engaged in washing dishes.

Mrs. Whitman said to her cheerily, "Well, Mary Ann, do you think you can love all these sisters?"

Mary Ann gave a little nod but did not speak, the dishes seeming to absorb her entire attention.

Seating herself in an armchair, Mrs. Whitman took little Louisa upon her lap and, calling the others around her, began to question them. Sis, shy and awkward in her embarrassment, stood di-

rectly in front, with arms akimbo, but her honest
eyes met Mrs. Whitman's clearly, and the pathos
of her story stirred to pity the woman who had
herself known deep sorrow.

"What is your name, dear?" was the first question.

"Catherine Sager," replied Sis.

"And your sisters are—?"

"Elizabeth, Matilda, and Hannah Louisa; and
our baby sister is called Henrietta."

"But where is the baby?"

"We left her with Mrs. Eads, she was so awful
sick. They think maybe she'll die; perhaps she is
dead by this time," and Sis's lip quivered.

"Oh, but that is too bad!" said Mrs. Whitman,
and added to herself, "I wanted the baby more than
all the rest."

Further questions revealed all the sad incidents
of that summer of sickness, death, and privation.

"You are indeed living in a hard time," said
Mrs. Whitman, "but let us trust that happier days
will come to you. We will help each other all we
can. You may begin, Catherine, by sweeping out
the buttery for me."

She showed the little girl where the broom was
kept and where she was to sweep, and Sis—or
Catherine, as she was always called in Dr. Whitman's family—did her best to please her new
friend. Later she was delighted to hear Mrs.
Whitman say to Mary Ann, "How well Catherine

sweeps!" Then came the setting of the table for the noon meal in the clean kitchen.

While Catherine was busy with this work, little Louisa played contentedly on the floor with a homemade toy Mrs. Whitman had found for her.

Presently in came a youth who sat down, looking curiously at the four little girls, but not addressing any of them; instead, he began conversation in the Indian language with Mrs. Whitman, whom he called "Aunt." He was Perrin Whitman, a nephew of Dr. Whitman's, and he made his home with his uncle and aunt. At this time he was but a boy of fourteen or fifteen and was at the awkward age. In fact, his pleasant face and well-shaped head were surmounted with such a long-drawn-out neck that the Indians called him "Qui-qui-tan-a-wat," or "Long Neck."

"Well, who are our visitors, if you please?" said a new voice and the children looked up to see a man standing in the doorway. Both arms were extended and the hands rested slightly above his head on the framework of the doorway. He was a stocky, well-built man, of good average height and his keen gray eyes looked pleasant, and at that moment, somewhat quizzical. He wore buckskin pants, a straw hat was on his head, well pushed back from the high forehead, and a slight but even sprinkling of gray hairs showed among the black. In place of a coat, he wore a "round-about"—a sort of vest with sleeves.

Instinctively the children knew this must be the good man in whom their parents had put such faith, and in whose care they were to remain.

Mrs. Whitman looked up at her husband with a welcoming smile. "Come in and get acquainted with your new family, Doctor," she said brightly. "Catherine is the oldest and Louisa is the smallest, and here are Elizabeth and Matilda. Matilda is lame, you see, and so you have work in your own special province at once. Catherine is somewhat lame, too, from a broken leg."

Dr. Whitman slowly crossed the floor and sat down near his wife, looking kindly at the strangers. "But where are the boys?" he asked, "And the baby?"

"The boys are at the mansion-house with the German doctor. You know we agreed about them," said Mrs. Whitman quickly. "I'm so disappointed over the baby. She is very ill and was left with the family that had been caring for her. If she had only been brought here, I wonder if you could not have cured her. I wanted her so much."

"I suppose you do want the girls, but I want those boys," said Dr. Whitman.

"They're mighty nice boys, Doctor," broke in Captain Shaw. "They've acted like men since the trouble came, and they're over yonder," nodding his head in the direction of the mansion-house, "just about breakin' their hearts to have to leave their sisters with strangers."

"I don't wonder at that," observed the Doctor gently.

Louisa, by this time, had forgotten her fright and was again on the floor playing.

"Come and see me, won't you, little one?" said Dr. Whitman, reaching out his arms to her.

But shyness overcame the little girl, and she again scurried to Catherine, crying, when she realized the strange man was speaking to her.

"There," laughed his wife, "now you've done it!"

The Doctor looked somewhat chagrined, for he was fond of children, and they were usually equally fond of him.

"*You'll* come, won't you?" said he, turning to Matilda. "You're not afraid of me."

Something in the strong but winning face attracted Matilda, and she went unhesitatingly toward him and allowed him to lift her to his lap. Some memory of her dead father moved her and in a minute or two her little arms were around the Doctor's neck, and her head was on his broad shoulder.

"There! You see I don't scare all of them," he remarked, with a whimsical look in his wife's direction. "We'll be good friends, won't we, little one?" he said, patting Matilda's tangled hair.

Soon Mrs. Whitman excused herself and became busy looking after the dinner which was served not long after. The grown-up people ate first, and to the half-fed children it was quite a trial of patience to wait until the older ones had satisfied hearty appetites. But they partly forgot the pangs of hunger in watching the other children who came quietly into the kitchen during the meal, and who were evidently waiting their turn at the bountiful table.

Mary Ann Bridger, whom the missionary Munger had brought to the Mission in '42, was the girl whom the children had found washing dishes. She was about Catherine's size and as they learned later, was a half-breed. She was especially fond of the Doctor and was nicknamed "Father's shadow" by the rest of the family. But the nickname in no way caused her to diminish her devotion to the kind friend she loved so well.

There was also the little one who had come with Mrs. Whitman to the wagon when they arrived. She had been left with Mrs. Whitman when but two or three years old, and at first the half-wild child did not take kindly to the ways of white people. Her Indian mother had accustomed her to sleep near the warm ashes of the fire in the tepee which had been her home, and child though she was, she could see no attractiveness in a bed, and for a long time would leave it and curl up like a kitten or puppy near the fireplace. So determined was she in this way of sleeping that it became necessary to sew her into her sheets and blankets for the night. But gradually she became used to white ways and developed into an unusually bright and attractive little girl, entering into everything with an energy that was amusing to the two friends who looked after her so carefully.

A thin-faced little boy, whom the other children called David Cortez, was another member of the family at that time. He, too, had a sad story behind his earliest years. Cruelly neglected and abused by his half-savage mother, a Walla Walla Indian, he had been starved and beaten and finally thrown naked into an empty cache to die alone. The Indian grandmother, knowing of the tender-hearted missionaries, and feeling a sympathy for the unfortunate baby that she dared not openly show, went by stealth to the cache, tucked the almost dying child under her blanket, and brought him to Dr. Whitman. It was long before he recovered from the shocking treatment of his unnatural mother; but the kind Doctor and his wife finally nursed the frail life into sturdiness.

"Seems to me they eat an awful lot," whispered little hungry Matilda to Catherine.

"Hush-h-h!" commanded Catherine in a spasm of fear lest her sister's remark be overheard. "They're most through, I reckon."

Much to the hungry child's relief, the children were soon bidden to the table. Nothing ever tasted quite so good as the well-boiled beef, the mealy potatoes, the turnips and cabbage, and the sweet, wholesome bread and butter, with milk for the younger ones.

Nothing had ever tasted so good.

Dr. Whitman remained indoors and helped wait upon his hungry brood.

"Mercy on us, children!" said Mrs. Whitman reprovingly. "You must eat more slowly and not cram so. I can't have my little girls eat like the Indian girls. See how nicely Mary Ann handles her knife and fork."

The sensitive Catherine lifted tear-blurred eyes to Mrs. Whitman's face. "Please excuse them this time, ma'am. We've et in such a hurry for so long, I expect we have most forgot how to do it nice."

"Never mind, Mother," laughed the Doctor. "You can teach them the niceties later. I'm most concerned that they don't stuff themselves like little pigs, for if they do, we'll have plenty of work on our hands."

It was a delight to this man to be able to give wholesome food to these forlorn children, but his physician's training told him the danger of over-feeding. "Hold on there!" he said smilingly to Matilda, as she asked for her fourth slice of bread. "I can see that I'll have to enlarge the capacity of my gristmill, but I can do that easier than you can enlarge your dinner basket. We will have another meal today and you'd better wait awhile."

Captain Shaw looked on smilingly. "Ah, but it does my heart good to see 'em! And it would their brothers', too. Many's the time them boys has put food in their sisters' mouths that they would have liked and needed for themselves. They're good boys, they are."

"We'll go over and see them," said the Doctor, leaving the children to Mrs. Whitman's care. "Do you know," he continued, as he and Captain Shaw followed along the path bordered by the autumn grass and flowers, "I'm very much disappointed not to keep the boys, but I realize fully how much my wife has on her hands and how hard it would be for her to have two hearty lads to do for, in addition to what she already has. Still, they would be of much use and at the same time protection, for I'm often away. Of course, we do not expect any trouble with the Indians, who seem very kind and friendly, but some day this valley will need strong men to people it, and I would be glad to think I had had a helping hand in placing these two here. For from what you tell me, I feel that they will develop into good and sturdy men."

"As I've told you before, two better boys never lived. They have shown enough grit and patience to make men of them already," said the Captain earnestly.

The two men found the boys sitting on a log just outside the door. They rose respectfully at their approach. It was easy to see that they were unhappy, for traces of tears still lingered around eyes swollen with crying.

"Had your dinner, boys?" asked Dr. Whitman.

"Yes, sir; that is, Dr. Dagin cooked some, but we didn't feel much like eating," answered John.

"I suppose you're so eager to go on, you don't feel like stopping to eat," said the Doctor.

John made no reply. How could he, when a big lump was working in his throat, threatening to choke him? It took all his powers to keep his eyes straight and steady, looking toward the hills clothed so beautifully and mistily with the haze of late autumn.

Beyond those hills he seemed to see a lonely stretch of land, the claim he and Frank might hope to secure, the battered wagon still their home, but with no sign of life near it, save two lonely, homesick boys going about their daily work. No helpful Sis to prepare their meals, no lame Tilda for them to help, no Lisbet to keep out of mischief. The outlook was large and empty and desolate.

The silence seemed almost vibrant with remonstrance against the hand of Fate, as the little group

stood there quietly, the Doctor's keen eyes intent
upon the sad faces of the boys.

"I'll tell you what I'll do, my boys," the Doctor
said at last with an air of finality. "If I can persuade Mrs. Whitman, you boys shall stay here this
winter and go to school; and then in the spring,
we'll talk about your taking up some land. How
will that suit you?"

Had Heaven been kind after all? John still
looked for an instant into space, but he no longer
saw the dismal picture that had held his mind's eye
but a moment ago, for human sympathy, strong
and helpful, had brought a film of tears to shut it
out. They were tears of joy, though, with wonderful lights in them.

"Oh, sir, if we might!" he said, unsteadily. "We
would do all we could for you and make as little
trouble for Mrs. Whitman as possible. It would
seem like leaving our life here, to leave our sisters
behind, though of course, we are ready to do what
is best for them."

"Very well, then, come over to the house with me
and I feel sure you will find a friend in Mrs. Whitman," said the Doctor. "Captain Shaw and I will
then draw up an agreement and everything will be
made right for both sides."

Mrs. Whitman finally acceded—rather reluc-
tantly, it is true—to her husband's wishes, and it
was decided that the boys were to remain.

Dr. Dagin with characteristic unselfishness ap-

proved heartily, forgetting to think of his own lone-
liness, for he had counted on keeping the boys with
him.

It was settled that the boys were to have the
stock and the girls were to have the household
goods. Dr. Whitman also agreed to exchange cows
for the steers belonging to the boys, and they were
to have the natural increase for their own also,
thus giving them a start in material things; and
they were to remain at the Mission that winter and
as much longer as they might agree.

Captain Shaw urged the Whitmans to adopt the
orphan family, but they declined to decide that
point at once. However, it was with a lighter heart
than he had had for many a day that the sturdy
Captain took his way back to join his own family
on their way to The Dalles and the Willamette
Valley.

# Chapter 10

# The Runaway Boys

THE BOYS soon found work in their new home. The cows had to be rounded up and milked and driven to and from their pasture, wood prepared, and water brought, and then there were countless errands to do for Dr. and Mrs. Whitman and for Elizabeth Felix, Mrs. Whitman's hired girl. So handy was John in the kitchen that later, in the early winter, when Miss Felix decided to go to Mrs. Spalding at Lapwai Mission, he was able under Mrs. Whitman's supervision to do most of the cooking the rest of the winter.

One morning a few days after their arrival, Catherine, who was in the sitting room, heard Mother Whitman, as she had begun to call her new friend, speak her name in a peculiar tone of voice, and she went to the kitchen quickly, wondering what was wanted. "Did you call me, Mother?" she asked.

"Yes, Catherine. See if you know who this little child is."

Catherine looked across the room where a woman sat beside the stove in a rocking chair, with a small child lying across her knees. She went slowly towards the group and it dawned upon her that the feeble, wasted baby was none other than her own little sister Henrietta, left, apparently dying, in the Eads wagon. It must be, for Mrs. Eads was holding it, and there was Louisa Eads sitting on the settee which stood in the huge, unused fireplace.

"We thought maybe Dr. Whitman could save her life, Sis," said Mrs. Eads, "so we just pulled over here to give her the chance."

"I'm so glad you did, for I can't tell you how much I wanted this baby, and we'll do all we can to save her, Mrs. Eads," said Mrs. Whitman. "Let me take her."

"Here's what's left of that dress you gave us for Baby," said Louisa Eads, exhibiting a small piece of cloth with charred edges. "We washed it and hung it up to dry too near the fire, or the wind carried sparks to it, or something; anyway, it caught fire and this is all that we could save." It was the dress that had been taken from the Sager boxes, to use as a shroud for Baby.

"Now, with God's blessing and what the Doctor can do, she'll not need it," said Mrs. Whitman.

Mrs. Eads, only too thankful to have the little one in more experienced hands than her own, took her way to the mansion-house to rest a few days before going farther.

So it came about that all of the Sager children—seven in number—were reunited again under the kind guardianship of Dr. and Mrs. Marcus Whitman.

It was the brightest spot among the many dark tragedies of pioneer days that there were so many kind people ready to give a helping hand to the

neighbors less fortunate than they. There were
no orphan asylums in that wild country, and often
the problem of returning homeless children across
a continent to relatives back East was an insuper-
able one; but, as the Sager children found, there
was always someone ready to take on the extra care
of more children, the necessity of a few more
mouths to feed.

Among these kind people, Dr. and Mrs. Marcus
Whitman were of course outstanding. Marcus
Whitman was a man whose thoughts from early
manhood had turned to the ministry. He was dis-
suaded from this desire, however, and instead,
turned to medicine. He first practiced his profes-
sion in Canada for four years, but in 1828 returned
to his native state and settled in Wheeler, New
York, which was the home of Judge Prentiss,
father of Miss Narcissa Prentiss. The young doctor
and Narcissa, who was renowned for her beauty,
soon became fast friends and were engaged to be
married. They were both much interested in missions, in fact, Miss Prentiss had at one time wished
to become a missionary.

At this time the story of the Flathead Indians
who came to St. Louis asking teachers for their
people "that they might learn of the white man's
God," had aroused much interest all through the
East. It was in 1832 that the chiefs had pleaded
earnestly to take the "White man's book of Heaven"
back to their people, and in 1834 the Methodists

sent the Lees to Oregon, where they became the advance guard of the Willamette Valley settlement.

In 1835 the American Board of Missions sent Dr. Marcus Whitman and Rev. Samuel Parker to Oregon on a trip of discovery. After a long, arduous journey, they returned East, Dr. Whitman fired with zeal and interest in the cause. It was not difficult for himself and Miss Prentiss to agree that here was a field of work worthy of their best efforts; and they set the wedding day and planned to leave early in 1836.

Two Indian boys from the far-off wilderness had accompanied Dr. Whitman East; and during the winter, Richard and John, as he called them, attended school, learning to speak and read English.

The Board thought it unwise for the young couple to start alone and asked them to defer their departure until companions could be found to go with them. The delay was not a long one, for they were fortunate in learning of the Rev. H. H. Spalding, who was about to start work at the Osage Mission. Without much urging, they finally decided to go with the Whitmans to the Far West.

Assured of company to their far distant mission, Narcissa Prentiss and Marcus Whitman were married in February, 1836, and they, with Mr. and Mrs. Spalding and the two Indian boys, left almost immediately for Oregon. It was not an easy trip. They went by steamboat down the Ohio and up the Mississippi and Missouri as far as Council

Bluffs, from which point the American Fur Company was to start a company of traders west upon a certain day. The Whitman party had been enlarged by a young man, W. H. Gray, and also by two teamsters. Fancy their perplexity and troubled feelings to find, on arriving at Council Bluffs, that the American Fur Company's party of traders and trappers had already departed. They decided that by forced marches they would attempt to overtake them.

It was not for some time that the little party, hampered with stock, overtook the larger company; but they finally did in May, and while some of the rough plainsmen were somewhat averse to having women in the company, the gentleness, patience, and courage of Mrs. Whitman and Mrs. Spalding soon won their hearts.

After a long trip, filled with interesting experiences, they arrived on September 1, 1836, at Fort Walla Walla. They soon after took the three-hundred-mile river trip with their husbands to Vancouver to consult with Dr. McLoughlin as to the best place to start the missions.

By his advice, it was finally decided to build one mission at Waiilatpu ("Land of Rye Grass"), twenty-five miles from Fort Walla Walla, among the Cayuse and Walla Walla Indians; and the other, one hundred and twenty-five miles farther on, among the Nez Perces at Lapwai.

Mrs. Whitman and Mrs. Spalding were guests

at Fort Vancouver while their husbands were engaged in visiting these localities and making the best arrangements possible for the comfort of their families. These were necessarily very crude, and the Spaldings were obliged to spend the first winter in a tepee. Dr. Whitman managed to make a very small and rude house, with boards whip-sawed by hand; but energy and industry accomplished so much that by December this modest building was ready for its occupants. In the days that followed, acres of land were put under cultivation. Sawmill and gristmill were built later and before the eyes of the Indians was spread an example of the white men's thrift and industry.

When the Sager children, in the autumn of 1844, arrived at the Mission to find shelter and a good home, there was much there for them to enjoy as well as to learn. The evenings before the early bedtime, when Mrs. Whitman would tell stories, were very pleasant. It was at this time, too, that they received instruction in singing; for it was a

regular custom to have daily instruction in vocal
music and it was not long before they could sing
easy songs and hymns with spirit and precision.

The story of Matilda's doll Betty and of her
sudden disappearance, had interested Mrs. Whitman, and one evening she said to the little girls, "If
you will sing extra well tonight, I will see if I cannot make you some dolls afterward."

The singing went with a vim, and later the important work of the dolls was begun. First the
bodies were cut out and sewn, only a little opening
being left to insert the stuffing. But what should
they stuff them with? Cotton was not plentiful in
the wilderness and what else was there?

"I think some bran will do very well and the
dollies will not mind if they do not look just like the
store dolls," said Mrs. Whitman. "They will not
complain loud enough for you to hear them, anyway."

After the dolls had been filled with their bran
stuffing, came the painting of eyes, noses, mouths,
and ears. Mrs. Whitman had some paints and did
it with some degree of skill.

That winter the school, from which Mr. and Mrs.
Sager had hoped so much for their children, was
started at the Mission. From the children's point
of view, it was not such a great success. Unfor-
tunately, a teacher was engaged who, though outwardly a kind and religious man, had a very cruel
streak in him. He quite outwore the adage "Spare

The dolls were filled with bran stuffing.

the rod and spoil the child" and outwore the patience of the children too.  At least Frank, the most
independent and rebellious of them, decided in the
spring that he could stand it no longer.

The winter under the stern rule of the fiery
schoolmaster had been for him a long, hard, and
unhappy one, and the constant work upon the farm
since the close of school had made him somewhat

discontented. Another boy somewhat older than himself also constantly told him that he was made to work too hard, and that, free from the restraint unjustly put upon him by the Whitmans, he would be able to have a much better time. At last Frank was fired with the determination to strike out for himself and win his own way. His love for his sister Matilda made him hesitate long before taking such a step. But one day his tempter, John Howard, had said, "Now, Frank, if ye're goin' with me, yer can't dillydally any longer. I'm off tomorrow mornin'. It's jest as yer feel, only I'm blamed if I'd be druv around like you be. And now's jest the time, while the old man's away. There won't be another missionary meetin' for a month and this is our best chance."

"But it's a long way to walk and I do so hate to leave my sisters," objected Frank.

"Walk nothin'! Think yer see me walkin'? Ain't yer leavin' stock behind that's wuth a couple o' cayuses? An' yer don't seem to be doin' much for yer sisters by jest stayin' here. Yer can work this year an' next an' somehow or other git some land and make a home fer 'em. Be yer own man, I say."

So very early next morning, Frank called to Matilda, asking her to come out in the yard. The family was all astir but had not breakfasted.

Matilda left her work wonderingly and went out as her brother had asked.

"Now, promise you won't say nothing, Tilda,"

said Frank impressively, when he had drawn her out of earshot of the open door, "but I can't stand it here any longer and I'm just going to run away. I won't forget you, and when I'm a man, I'm coming back to take you away, too."

"Oh, *don't*, Frank! Don't think of such a thing! You mustn't! Why, I'd cry my eyes out 'cause I'd want to see you so bad," and Matilda tried to clasp her arms about the neck of her tall brother.

He quickly undid the clasping arms, for he did not want to attract attention to his movements by any unusual demonstration. But he said decidedly, "It won't do any good—I'm going, that's all! Now, be a good girl and by and by you may tell the rest and say good-by for me. If Mother Whitman suspects what I'm doing, she will fix it so I can't get off." And with a final pat on the head, he walked quickly in the direction of two horses tethered at some distance from the house, down by the big wheat field.

Matilda, heartbroken and distracted, threw herself sobbing on the ground, where she was found a little later by Catherine.

She refused to say what troubled her, but her sister, casting her eyes around the four points of the compass to discover, if possible, what was causing Matilda to behave in that way, saw in the distance two fast disappearing figures on horseback and the truth flashed upon her.

"Is that Frank and is he running away?" she

Not wishing to attract attention, Frank quickly undid the clasping
hands.

fairly screamed in her excitement. "And why didn't you stop him?" Then without waiting for more than an affirmative nod from the weeping Matilda, she rushed back to the house, calling, "Mother Whitman! Mother Whitman! Frank is running away with John Howard!"

Mother Whitman came to the kitchen door with a most perplexed look on her gentle face. "Oh, the poor misguided boy," she said. "But we mustn't let him go. We can't spare him and for his own sake we must overtake him and bring him back. Oh, if the Doctor were only here! Go call John, some of you, and tell him to saddle a horse and follow as fast as he can. Tell him to ride around by the door and I'll have some food all put up for him."

John was some distance away milking their cows and his view of the proceedings had been quite cut off by the buildings. He quickly left his task, the deserted cow watching him over her shoulder, switching her tail from side to side, evidently wondering why she had been left in such unseemly haste. The half-wild horses in their pasture were not easily caught. They had already had one race with the two runaway boys, and were wide awake and ready for more fun.

So in spite of John's clever coaxing and adroit maneuvering, some time passed before he had a saddle on one of them and was at the door, ready for the package of food which he tied to his saddle.

"Do your best to find them and tell Frank we love him too much to have him leave us this way," called Mrs. Whitman as he started off rapidly.

"I'm afraid he'll not overtake them," said Catherine sadly, "for they had a long start and it is so easy to lose the trail. They'll do all they can to mislead our John and John Howard knows lots about such things. And then there are so many of the little rolling hills that it will be a wonder if he even catches sight of them."

The long day passed in a fever of anxiety to the household. Would the elder brother bring Frank back, or if he found him, would the latter persuade John to join him and both go on to the Willamette? Instinctively, Catherine said "No" to this thought, for she felt in her heart that sober John would never entertain such an idea, but still there was a certain anxiety in her mind on this point that would not down.

Just as dusk was falling, John rode up alone, his horse jaded and not looking much like the lively little cayuse of the early morning hours.

"I didn't even catch a glimpse of them, though I followed their trail for a long distance," he said. "Finally I lost it and though I crisscrossed ever so many times, I couldn't pick it up again. There seemed to be nothing to do but to come back, for I could not leave all you folks alone here tonight."

John looked tired and dejected enough. It had been a struggle for him to know what to do. His inclination was to follow the runaway until he found him; but on the other hand, there was Mother Whitman and the children left in his care and duty seemed to point him back to the Mission. For while the Indians seldom became unruly or obnoxious, he knew that Father Whitman believed his wife and the little children safer from annoyance if they had a masculine protector. So back he came, wishing in his heart he could get his hands on his lively brother long enough to shake a little sense into his head.

"We have done all we could, John. Don't look so blue," comforted Mrs. Whitman. "The Doctor will be home tomorrow and most likely he will send for him. Eat your supper and go to bed, for you look worn out."

The earnest prayer for the fugitive found an echo in every heart at devotions that night; but in spite of the comfort of the prayer, more than one pillow was wet with secret tears; for it seemed to Catherine, Matilda, and Elizabeth that their unforgotten troubles of the previous year were beginning over again.

Dr. Whitman returned about the middle of the following day. He had heard a rumor of their trouble from an Indian whom he had met a few miles from home, and his face looked stern as he discussed the runaways with his wife and John. "No," he said decidedly, "he must not be sent for. He has done wrong and must be made to realize it. At first, I thought I would start right off after him, but thinking it over as I came along, I decided it would be the worst possible thing to do. Let him stay until he learns what he has given up. We will send word to him that he may come back if he wishes, and in that way let him decide for himself what he most wants. And we'll not talk of him or discuss his action any further."

So it came about that Frank's name was very seldom mentioned in the summer days that followed.

But one morning in the following October when the children were busily at work in the big kitchen, all at once the door opened and Frank stepped hesitatingly inside. No one but the children were in the room and the vociferous welcome they gave him must have been very sweet and reassuring. How the tongues did run! But into the joyous hubbub a sudden tense silence fell as the door opened to admit Mrs. Whitman.

Frank edged forward awkwardly on his chair, evidently feeling very uncertain as to his reception by her. But the motherly heart did not leave him long to wonder. With outstretched arms she went to him, saying, "My dear boy, I'm glad you have come home again," while her tender kiss of welcome took from Frank's heart any sting of uncertainty. He returned her greeting with genuine feeling.

From that moment they became trustful, sincere friends and she received from him the loyal feeling and the thoughtful devotion that her motherly love for him deserved. Dr. Whitman was equally kind, though less demonstrative in his greeting, and it was not many days before the runaway had resumed his accustomed place in the family circle.

# Chapter 11

# Life at Dr. Whitman's Mission

WITH Frank back with them once more, life resumed its normal course at the Mission. There was plenty of work for all to do—weaving, sewing, cooking, sweeping for the girls, with outdoor work in plenty for the boys. The younger girls were working on patchwork, but Catherine was old enough to help in keeping the family clothed. This, with a family of the size of that at the Mission, was no small task.

There were constant breaks in Mrs. Whitman's days, for even if her own family was well and busy, someone always wanted her help or advice. Some Indian mother would often slip silently into the Indian room, a room never used by the whites, but set aside for the use of their dusky friends. If none of the family found her there and inquired her needs, she would come to the kitchen, slip in without ceremony and ask aid for a sick or injured papoose, carried, if very ill, under her gaudy blanket, or if only slightly ailing, in a parfleche of undressed oxhide on her back. If Dr. Whitman was away, then Mrs. Whitman had to do the best she could to allay the sufferings or injuries of the little one.

It was a heavy burden for her, for the Indians were very superstitious, and there was the ever-present danger that a little patient might become worse suddenly, and the ignorant parents would

attribute the change to her. Still, how could she refuse to do what she could for a suffering child?

Then there were the Indians who came to barter
berries or fish or game for some of the Mission's
stores. This was a job requiring both patience and
tact.

One day Prince, one of their Indian neighbors,
appeared in the kitchen. He was not a chief, as his
name might indicate, but was called Prince by the
whites, because of his tall form and stately way of
carrying himself. In his hand he held a tin coffeepot filled with blackcap raspberries.

"Me come for flour," he announced without pre-
lude, holding out the berries.

"Very well, Prince," replied Mrs. Whitman, tak-

ing the berries and emptying them into a dish. She
gave him more flour in quantity than she had received berries, and he started off as quietly as he
had come.

Mrs. Whitman resumed her work, but five minutes later looked up to see Prince standing in the
doorway.

"Me no want flour; me take beans," he said. So the exchange was made and off he went the second time.

Ten minutes elapsed and again he reappeared. "Rice all better as beans. Rice make good muck-a-muck," was his remark this time.

"But I've very little rice and cannot give you as much as I have of the beans," objected Mrs. Whitman.

"Rice good for Prince," he said, looking very determined.

The Doctor was away and it seemed best to comply with his wish for rice, so a small quantity was given him and he disappeared, looking very gratified. It was not long before he again reappeared and holding out the rice disdainfully, said, "Not good measure. Want much heap rice."

"But I told you I could give you but a little rice, for we have but little and I want that in case someone is sick. Here are your berries," she said, putting them back in his coffeepot. "If you are not satisfied, take them back."

"No want berries. Got heaps up where *paw-paws* [bear] lives. No can see rice," and he squinted disdainfully at the rice Mrs. Whitman had just emptied from his dish.

"What do you want then? You must make your choice and not come back again this morning," said Mrs. Whitman, feeling that her patience had been tried far enough.

Prince studied his handsomely beaded moccasins awhile, then let his glance wander dreamily through the open window into space, and finally condescended to say, "Prince take potatoes this time."

So some potatoes were brought from the outside storeroom, but once more he changed his mind. "Flour best after all. Prince take flour," he remarked. So flour was given him and he left with exactly the same quantity he had first been given an hour before. Two minutes later, his head came through the door again. "Give Prince butter, too?" he questioned.

"Not this morning. Maybe when you bring berries next time." And off he went, silenced if not satisfied.

This incident was re-enacted with variations upon the days set apart for paying the Indians for any work they might have done upon the farm or around the buildings. A line of them would form in the yard and Dr. and Mrs. Whitman would go the length of it, asking each one what commodity he wished to be paid in. Then an experience like that just related of Prince would have to be gone through with nearly every individual in the line.

As the days turned toward the winter of 1845-46, the children began to think again of school. Would they have to undergo the torture of the previous winter, with a tyrant for a master? They feared that, in the absence of any other qualified person, it might be necessary to recall their former teacher from the Willamette Valley, whither he had gone in the spring.

"Tell you what," said Frank, as he stirred vigorously on the boiled wheat he was helping cook, "I'd rather die than go through what I did last winter."

But fortune favored them, for one day a Mr. Rodgers, a young men with a mild, pleasant face and winning ways, came to the Mission to try to make arrangements to have a friend, ill with consumption, brought there to receive the benefit of the Doctor's skill. He became interested in the life at the Mission and at the solicitation of Dr. Whitman decided to remain there and teach the school for that winter.

He was as fond of music as Mrs. Whitman and not only sang well, but also played the violin.

The schoolroom was a changed place, for under the kindly, encouraging rule of the new teacher, the young folks did their best. Frank, who had been so unhappy before, now enjoyed his books and worked with an earnestness and pleasure that won him praise from the master. A singing school was also taught every week by Mr. Rodgers.

So life went on at the Mission. It was not all work for the children, by any means. There were picnics in the summer and berry pickings, and swims in the river which ran near the house. But the main object of its establishment—the conversion and education of the Indians—was never lost sight of by the two brave missionaries who had given up the comfort and security of their life at home to accomplish this purpose.

That winter of 1845-46 was an unusually severe one, so severe that it worked hardship on the Mission. It also worked great hardships on the Indians round about, and they, in their primitive

The ponies wandered gaunt and hungry over the snow-covered ground.

reasoning, decided that the whites must be the cause of the unprecedented weather. Nothing like it had ever been known before the whites came, so of course it was the whites who caused it. Their ponies wandered, gaunt and hungry, over the snow-covered ground, unable to root out the bunch grass hidden away under the white, frosty covering.

"We have deserted our gods for the faith of the

white man and this is the result," was the wail that went up, as frigid nights succeeded freezing days.

In their extremity, they appealed to old Jimmy, a Catholic Indian, who was popularly credited with the ability to work miracles. They paid him liberally to bring about a thaw; and a thaw really did put in an appearance—for a day or two. But it was shortly as cold as ever and the foxy old fellow assured his tribespeople that they had not paid him enough to secure lasting results. It took much more of skins, beads, and other things dear to an Indian's heart, to break such a spell as this. So his friends made him another donation, far more liberal than the first, and soon the final thaw, the forerunner of spring, came to strengthen their faith in their old superstitions, at the same time rooting a little deeper their suspicions of the white man.

In March the Spaldings, the missionaries who had come West with the Whitmans, came to visit at Waiilatpu for a few days. These infrequent visits were about the only social diversion of the two isolated missionary wives. The Spaldings remained several days and when they at last declared they must start homeward, so reluctant were their friends to part with them that Mrs. Whitman said, "It doesn't seem as though we had seen half enough of you. If you really must go, I've a mind to suggest to the Doctor that we go part way with you and camp out for a day or two at Log City."

The children were in raptures of excitement when it was finally decided that the trip was really to be taken.

The face of Nature was turning green, and early flowers were already showing starry blooms, so sudden had been the transition from winter to balmy spring days. Birds and wind seemed trying to outsing each other in the low and tender spring chant.

Tents and bedding were piled into an oxcart, also provisions and the necessary dishes. The only cooking utensils was the frying pan, for the potatoes could be roasted in the ashes. Coffee and tea were not used even on such an occasion as this.

Skillful from long practice, Frank drove the ox team with its load safely to the destination, without any mishap to the squirming, laughing youngsters who formed a part of it.

A charming spot was selected to make camp, a place beside a creek, over which the bending trees reached their branches. That it was a favorite camping place with others as well as themselves, was shown by blackened embers, marking the spot where fish, fresh from the pools and shadows of the stream, had been broiled.

Several rudely put together log huts were clustered near by. They had been erected by a party of settlers who had once wintered there, but who removed to the Willamette Valley in the following spring. They were standing deserted and decaying, but proved attractive to the children, who seemed to prefer them to the tent which had been brought along. It began to rain soon after they reached the place and it was cheery and comforting to start a blaze in one of the long-unused fireplaces.

With games and singing, the afternoon passed quickly for the children and it was time for evening devotions before they thought it possible.

"We must be up betimes for an early start towards Lapwai," remarked Mrs. Spalding, as goodnights were being said.

"And we will start towards Waiilatpu at the same time, I suppose," said Mrs. Whitman.

"Oh, Mother Whitman, it is so nice here, couldn't we stay just a little longer?" begged Elizabeth, her eyes shining with eagerness.

"Why don't you Mother? That's a good idea," broke in Dr. Whitman. "I'll have to go early but you can stay as well as not; it will do you all good."

Mrs. Whitman hesitated; but as the rest of the children all begged to remain longer, she finally sent them to bed happy with an affirmative answer.

The next morning was pleasant and the Spaldings left early. After their departure, the children tried to catch fish for their dinner and passed the time in games until a smart shower drove them to the shelter of a log hut and to the joys of an open fire. It was still early morning, for they had risen very early.

"My! Ain't this nice?" said Matilda, stretching

out like a kitten. "I'm afraid the Spaldings are getting wet. I'd like to stay here a long time where it's warm and dry."

"You're most likely to get your wish, Missy," said Frank, who stepped in quickly just then, with a troubled look on his face. "What do you suppose those pesky oxen have done?" he questioned Mrs. Whitman.

"Not run off, I hope?" she replied, looking anxious.

"That's just what!" responded Frank. "I couldn't see them when the Spaldings started, but thought they must be somewhere near. Since then I've hunted and hunted, and I can't find a trace of them, so they must have run off to the range. I'll have to go after them. Don't be worried if I'm not back real soon."

"That *is* too bad," said Mrs. Whitman, as Frank disappeared. "I suppose we're all right, but I feel safer to have Frank here. I do wish we could have started home when the Doctor and the Spaldings left. Frank may have a long hunt for the cattle."

"What can we do to pass the time while he's away? Oh, I know, let's sing some more," said Catherine.

"Yes, let's," chimed in Helen Meek, "and maybe those naughty oxen will come running back to listen to us," she said roguishly.

Song after song was sung with vivacity and they were just about to begin on another, when Elizabeth held up her hand with a gesture for silence. "Seems to me I hear something coming."

"Most likely it's the oxen, wanting to hear us sing," giggled Helen.

" 'Tain't oxen," objected Catherine. "It's a quicker sound than oxen would make. It's a thump, thump, thumpity-thump, more like horses than oxen."

"Maybe it's loose stock that belongs to the Indians," suggested someone.

"Stop talking, children, so we can listen a bit," commanded Mrs. Whitman.

Instant silence fell and uneasy glances were exchanged, as the rhythmic beat of many hoofs came very distinctively to their strained ears. Whatever it might be, it was evidently heading in their direction and coming rapidly at that.

"We must find out what it is," said Mrs. Whitman. She was outwardly calm and serene, but inwardly was thinking, "What can I possibly do to protect these little ones? Suppose it should be hostile Indians coming over the mountain to attack our peaceful settlements? It can't be—but it might!" She stepped outside the door and was closely followed by the children who huddled behind her, dreading to really discover what this danger might be.

It took but a moment to see that a large band of Indians was rapidly approaching.

"Do you recognize any of them?" said Mrs.

Whitman, turning to Catherine. Her voice quivered a little as she spoke, for she realized that there was no possible way of escape, and that in a few seconds' time they would all be at the mercy of the party of savages.

"They're too far off for me to see faces," said Catherine. "Only I can see that it is a band of braves without their women and children."

A moment or two later they were in the midst of the band, who checked their ponies and threw themselves from their backs, evidently astonished to find a white woman and several small children occupying a favorite camping spot.

"They are Nez Perces and we are all right, I hope," said Mrs. Whitman as the leader came up to them.

"Oh, there's Ellis," broke in Matilda excitedly. "We know him."

Ellis paid no attention to this, though he must have heard, but shook hands gravely with the lady. He then extended his hand to the little girl, who put hers out, but at the same time cast her eyes to the ground in embarrassment.

"How's this?" said the stately looking warrior sternly. "Why is it that the paleface maiden cannot look her friend in the face? Among my people, it is a straight look from the eye and from the heart that the eye mirrors—a straight, level look that speaks true, whether it tells of friendship or of hate. No hiding behind the curtain, thinking none can tell what goes on within, with the Nez Perces. But the children fall into bad ways and think there is no need of doing fairly with their elders. Is it not so?"

"The white children love the good and hate the bad, like the children of our Indian friends. But they are shy like the antelope of the plains, in the presence of mighty hunters," said Mrs. Whitman, shrewdly guessing that the unexpected arrivals were on a hunting trip.

She spoke with quietness, for among the dusky faces she had had time to recognize one of the two Indian boys who had gone East with the Doctor in 1835. Seeing Richard, knowing that he was a firm friend of the Doctor's, and having full faith in the good intentions of the whole Nez Perce tribe, she felt reassured. She also recognized the face of Tom Hill, a Delaware, a man of power and influence among the members of his adopted tribe.

"May the buffalo which we go to hunt not prove as shy as the two children of the Great Spirit you mention—the antelope and the young maiden," said Ellis with a relaxing of the grimness of his face.

"When do you go on?" queried Mrs. Whitman, speaking in his own language.

"We are in no hurry and will stay here until the sun again rides his cayuse. Now the clouds hide his way, but will soon be gone," said the chief. "Then we go to Waiilatpu to talk with our good

friend Dr. Whitman. After that, we hasten to
the hunting grounds beyond the big mountains."

After a short time the Indians left and early
morning brought Frank and the truant oxen, and
the homeward way was taken. On arriving at
Waiilatpu, they found their Nez Perce friends of
the previous day assembled there and Dr. Whitman
preparing to give them a feast that evening.

"Just in time to participate in the festivities of
the occasion," said he to his wife, with a twinkle in
his eye.

"I very much fear my absence will be more ap-
preciated than my presence," she returned laugh-
ingly, "and as I've no desire to eat at this table,
or to smoke either, I'll let you have that pleasure
alone. I will content myself with making the tea
for you."

The preparations were simple, quantity being
the first requisite. A huge fire was made in the
yard not far from the door of the Indian room,
and a thirty-gallon kettle of water swung from a
tripod over it; this was heated and into it was
stirred plenty of corn meal and also some tallow.
This was given a thorough cooking and then two
men carried it from the fire into the Indian room.
With much dignity and decorum, the chief, sub-
chiefs, and Dr. Whitman helped themselves from
the kettle, while the lesser lights of the tribe,
squatted upon the floor, contented themselves with
their portion served on tin plates. They would sit

The early morning brought Frank and the truant oxen.

in no other place, and the benches along the sides
of the room were occupied by Mr. Rodgers, the children, and some of the whites from the mansion-
house, as spectators.

Every atom was eaten, even what had been inad-
vertently dropped upon the floor! Some of the white
spectators were almost strangled in their efforts
to keep back their laughter when they saw the
frugal visitors groping around on the floor with
their horn spoons to make sure that no portion had
been overlooked. In fact, it was too much for the
little girls, and a half-suppressed giggle drew the
Doctor's attention in their direction. He looked
very stern as he motioned to them to leave the
room. It would have been a terrible affront to the
guests to have allowed any hilarity to become
apparent to them.

The little girls afterward discovered that the
Doctor was not seriously offended, for his own eyes
twinkled merrily at the remembrance of the occasion of their disgrace; but in spite of that, he impressed upon their minds the absolute necessity
of observing with scrupulous nicety the forms so
dear to the customs of their dusky friends.

In the sitting room, Mrs. Whitman made large
quantities of tea, putting much sugar in. The
seldom-used door between this room and the Indian
room was opened and some of the Indians carried
the beverage to their companions. When all were
served, Mrs. Whitman herself became one of the

spectators, for it would not do to have her entirely absent from so important an occasion. The tea seemed to loosen their eloquence, for, the last drops having been swallowed and a certain few having assured themselves that no more mush remained undiscovered upon the floor, cups and plates were laid aside and speech making began.

The Doctor assured them of their welcome and of his love and friendship for their tribe. The chief responded, saying, "The sun is at its zenith between our hearts. There can be no shadows, no suspicion of distrust, to make one afraid of the good will of the other."

Then Tom Hill arose and in full, deep tones gave with much native dignity a speech about education and the work the missionaries were doing in teaching the red man, not alone from the Book of God, but also from other books. "The sun should shine kindly and the wind blow softly upon those who spend their lives in teaching our minds and souls, so that we may follow the same trail as have the mighty ones who have gone before us. And the thunder god and the war god will frown upon those who do not remember this," he ended, carried away by his own eloquence and lapsing momentarily into an expression that proved that his early belief had not been entirely superseded by his later conversion to Christianity. A little later the party broke up, Nez Perces and whites alike pleased with the friendliness and good will of the other.

# Chapter 12

## *A Sinister Arrival*

THE SAME routine of work and play had kept the children busy in this summer of 1847 as in the two previous summers. They had all grown more capable and had become accustomed to the wise discipline of the Mission.

John and Frank were stout lads of seventeen and thirteen respectively; Catherine was almost thirteen and had entirely recovered the use of the broken leg; Elizabeth was ten, hearty, and well; and Matilda, two years younger, had practically outgrown her lameness, thanks to Dr. Whitman's skillful treatment. Hannah Louisa was six, a rollicking, happy child, with a strong inclination to have her own way whenever possible. Henrietta, the baby, everybody's pet, was three in May of that year. She had developed well under the loving

Work and play kept the children busy in the summer.

attention of the whole family, each member vying with the others to make up, in part, the loss she had sustained in the early weeks of her young life. Her birthday, as was the custom with every member of the household, was made noticeable by some in-dulgence—a little longer time to play or the singing of some of the especially liked songs. Perhaps some-one would have a new recitation to mark the day. If it was possible, the celebration took the form of a picnic—the form of recreation that appealed most to the children.

When a picnic was being planned, it was excit-ing just to watch the preparations that went on in the kitchen, for Mother Whitman always provided a special treat. Sometimes it was a huge goose-berry tart. But even if the treat was only plain cookies, the very rarity of any sort of sweets made the outing a festive occasion.

After the provisions were safely packed in bas-kets, Frank would push the two-wheeled cart to the door, and baskets and baby would be packed in and the start made. Usually the rest of the party walked, though sometimes Mrs. Whitman and one or two of the girls rode their horses.

The girls loved horseback riding, and Mrs. Whit-man, also fond of the exercise, was glad to have her little girls know the pleasure of being carried easily and swiftly over the ground by the wiry little cayuses.

Catherine could ride quite well, but one day she

"If you fall off, I'll whip you," John called.

came near a mishap. The pony she was riding became frightened in some manner and started to run. John, ever watchful where his sisters were concerned, whipped up his horse and tried to overtake the other pony. But the hurrying hoofbeats behind only served to accelerate the speed of Catherine's mount, and in spite of her best efforts, she was utterly unable to check his impetuous flight. The others stopped their ponies, holding their breath for fear the girl would be thrown. Matilda covered her eyes, but Elizabeth sat white-faced, looking helplessly after her sister. Even Mrs. Whitman, usually so resourceful, could do nothing but murmur a prayer for the life of her young charge. Meanwhile, the runaway horse sped on.

John, straining after, saw the slight form sway from side to side and though almost speechless with the fear gripping his heart, managed to shout after her just the words that steadied the frightened child. "If you fall off, I'll *whip* you," he called. "Remember, I'm just going to whip you, if you fall off that horse. Don't you dare!"

Catherine heard just as she was about to give up. "John *whip* me? Well, I reckon not," she thought to herself. "I'd like to see either of my brothers think they dare do that!" The thought made her so indignant, that she pulled with vigor at the bridle lines and to her surprise, the pony responded and came to a halt.

"I rather think you won't whip me, John Sager,"

she blazed at him, as her white-faced brother came
alongside.

John recovered his composure as he looked at
Catherine's flushed cheeks and eyes sparkling with
anger. "Learn to stay on your horse then," he
drawled. "Needn't be so mad though. If I'd told
you to be careful or look out, you'd have spilled
yourself off in no time, and we should have had the
job of picking parts of you up all the way back for
the last mile or so. What do you suppose I've got
five sisters for, if I hain't learned by this time that
girls are mighty queer and contrary?"

"I'll tell you right now, John Sager, I'd like to
see the boy that isn't full as contrary as any girl
you can name! So there!"

"Well," said John with a twinkle in his eye,
"you're safe and that's all I want."

About this time, a young fellow by the name of
Joe Lewis came with one of the emigrant wagon
trains to the Mission and applied to the Doctor for
work for the winter. The Doctor did not want him,
but as he was in evident distress, he got him a
position to go on from the Mission with another
train. At the end of three days he was back again,
having left his employers in the night to run back
to Waiilatpu. He was a swarthy, unkempt, unre-
liable-looking fellow—causing one of the children
to remark, "The Indians had better talk to him
about looking folks in the eye." No one seemed
to like him, for there was something about him that

Joe Lewis applied to the Doctor for
work.

repelled all the whites. The people of the train he
had come in with said he had been with them from
Fort Hall only, his previous fellow travelers having
become so incensed at his surly, disagreeable ways
that they turned him adrift, refusing to let him
travel with them any longer. He was in such sore
straits that he had hardly clothing enough to protect him.

"What do you need in the way of clothing?" the
Doctor asked him. "Have you an extra shirt?"

For answer, Lewis threw back his coat, exposing
his bare skin and proving conclusively that he not
only lacked an extra shirt, but even a single one to
cover his nakedness. He was also without socks
and his boots were so tattered and torn that there
were more holes than leather to be seen.

The Doctor, kind to everyone who needed kindness, regardless of their appearance, gave him some clothes and set him to work. It was noticed that he went often to the Indian village and appeared to be very friendly with them. It has been said of him that he was at least part Indian, born in Canada and brought up by white people in Maine. His coming to the mission marked the beginning of the train of events which led to final tragedy. There is no doubt but that he did everything in his power to injure the Whitmans, who in the kindness and goodness of their hearts were so charitable to him.

# Chapter 13

# The Warning

MEASLES and whooping cough had been brought to the West by the ever more frequent emigrant trains. Cases became numerous among the Indians, and as usual with their people, the measles were proving deadly.

So many were the calls upon Dr. Whitman that the family at the Mission saw but little of him, for he was going night and day, far and near, trying with all his skill to relieve the sufferings of his red charges. Doubtless he could have saved many if they had not persisted in treating their sick ones in their own way, on top of using the Doctor's medicines.

With the Indians, one of the most potent cures for all ills was a sweat bath, followed by a plunge into cold water, the colder the better. They would dig a good-sized hole in the ground, cover it over with a roof of skins and earth, drop into the hole a number of sizzling hot stones, and finally throw water on them to make clouds of steam arise. Then they would creep into the stifling place and stay until every pore was open and they were sweating profusely. Then they would run to near-by water and jump in. This treatment, good as it may have been for many ills, was the worst possible one for measles, as it caused the disease to "strike in," proving fatal in every case. One by one, the Indians saw members of their families succumb, and consternation reigned among them.

It was some satisfaction for them to know that the children of the whites were ill also, for day by day new cases developed among the people at the Mission and the mansion-house. John, Matilda, and then Catherine came down with the disease.

The Indians watched the course of the disease among their white neighbors very closely, evidently suspicious that they themselves were suffering from some other illness, or a far worse form of the same. In vain the Doctor explained to them that it was because of greater cleanliness and better nursing that none of his own family had died. They looked unconvinced and continued to watch suspiciously.

Timtimmisi, one of their chiefs, came to the Doctor one day. Dr. Whitman could see he had something to say and stopped to wait for him.

"Timtimmisi's heart sore," was his first remark.

"Our hearts are all heavy these days," rejoined the Doctor. "So much sorrow, so many sick and so much suffering makes us all grieve."

"The Shum Sitsmu-sitsmu say that you are causing us to die. That if we believe your words, we are all lost. I, myself, do not believe it, but many of my people do."

"That you know is not true. Can your people not see that I am doing all in my power to help and save you all? I am glad you still trust me, and

Timtimmisi.

you must tell your brothers that I love them too well to want to injure one of them."

"That Timtimmisi has done and will again do; but still, when the Great Spirit takes our dear ones, more and more, two, three, maybe five or six every day, then I hear the whisper like the hiss of our grandfather, the snake, saying, 'The good Doctor is good no longer; he is poisoning us.' As I said, I do not believe it, but I cannot make all my people think as I do."

"Do the best you can and they will realize the truth some time. The rest is in the hands of God," said the Doctor sadly.

No one knew the vacillating heart of the Indian nature better than he, or realized more than he the terrible power of a superstition over their actions. Both he and Mr. Spalding realized that they and their work were in serious peril; but not for an instant did they relax their efforts to do their best to help and lead their red charges to better things.

But the statement that the whites were the cause of all the sickness and suffering was repeated from mouth to mouth, and all the Indians, young and old, knew of it and talked of it and it made a great impression upon most of them.

One night when Mr. Spalding was visiting an Indian village, a niece of the chief died, and he requested Mr. Spalding to officiate at the funeral. The body was prepared for burial and put in a coffin made of a canoe cut into two pieces for box and lid. At the funeral Mr. Spalding noticed one of the young Nez Perces of his own mission. He was not surprised to see him, for there was a constant interchange of visits between neighboring tribes. This young fellow was a good friend of Mr. Spalding's and came to him with quite a confidential air, saying, "Has Dr. Whitman been killed yet?"

"Killed? What do you mean?"

But the fellow had nothing further to say and Mr. Spalding knew one might as well try to wrest secrets from the Sphinx as from an Indian, when he is not inclined to talk. So he had to leave for

As Doctor Whitman looked up suddenly from his patient he noticed Tamahas, who was crouched and bending slightly forward, as though ready to spring upon him.

Waiilatpu, without eliciting further information from him.

Only once since an unpleasant encounter with an Indian named Tamahas in the mill yard nearly three years before, had the Doctor seen any signs of active hostility on the part of an Indian; and it was this same surly fellow that he had recently again detected in an attitude that indicated violence.

Tamahas had just lost his wife by the epidemic, and the Doctor, who was attending other sick ones in the lodge, noticed, as he looked up suddenly from his patient, that Tamahas was crouched and bending slightly forward, as though ready to spring upon him. As soon as he saw the Doctor looking at him, he relaxed his position and pretended to be very closely examining something in his hand. The Doctor had seen enough, however, to cause him to keep a sharp watch upon him as long as he remained in the tepee and after that, he was more cautious among them.

One night a message came from Hezekiah or Five Crows, who lived at some distance from the Mission. "Five Crows wishes his good brother to come to the Umatilla and help make well the sick ones there. Will he come?" was the message brought by an Indian runner.

Without any hesitation, Dr. Whitman and Mr. Spalding—who happened to be at the Mission—started on a twenty-five mile trip in the darkness of the night, unmindful alike of the gloom and the pouring rain.

It was very late when they arrived at the lodge of Stickus. They were thoroughly wet, but as they were given a good place for their blankets before a cheery fire burning in his tepee, they felt ready when early morning came for the breakfast served by the wife of Stickus, after the regular family worship had been reverently held. The breakfast consisted of potatoes, squash, fresh beef, and wheat bread. "What a contrast the comfortable living among some of these people is to the wretchedness and starvation to which they were all subject eleven years ago," said the Doctor thoughtfully, as he finished his meal.

"And we owe it all to your showing us how the white man uses what lies at his hand. Yes, we owe much to you," said Stickus. "But there are those who love you not and might seek to do you harm," he added, lowering his tones to great softness as the Doctor rose to go.

"Who should seek to hurt me, Stickus?" questioned the Doctor.

"That Stickus does not surely know. He only hears a half whisper here and there, like the wind rising among the trees. But it is a sad sound and makes your friend feel heavyhearted."

"But I cannot desert my work for whispers. God surely will protect my family, and I am not afraid."

It was Sunday morning and the Doctor went

about among the sick all day. About four in the
afternoon, exhausted by his work among the sick
ones, he rejoined Mr. Spalding. He declared that in
spite of his weariness he must return at once to
Waiilatpu to attend the suffering ones there. So
he took but a few minutes to rest and about sun-
down prepared to start for home. As he mounted

Word was passed from mouth to
mouth that the whites were the cause
of all the sickness.

his horse, his host said to him, "Let me speak again
to you."

"What is it, my friend?"

"Stickus tells you true," said the Indian impressively. "My people are holding councils every night
and they say to each other, 'Shall we kill the Doctor
or not?' Some say 'No,' but more say 'Yes!' It is
Joe Lewis who is telling them that you are poisoning them and that that is what makes our people
die so fast."

"Do you believe it, Stickus?"

"Would your friend tell you this if he did? No, I do not believe it! We have never had any but good things from your hands, but Stickus warns his friend to be careful."

"Thank you, good friend. My life is in the hands of God. I am here to serve Him and He will direct. Good-by."

Stickus and Mr. Spalding watched him ride over the hill and disappear in the dim light. They were never to see him again.

# Chapter 14

## The Survivors

IT WAS Christmas Day at the Mission, and almost two months since the Indians had risen in fanatical and misguided hatred and killed Dr. and Mrs. Whitman, and twelve others of the inmates of the Mission, including the brave John and Frank Sager, who had died trying to defend their friends and their sisters. Little Hannah Louisa died shortly thereafter of the measles.

The two months since that terrible day had been lived as in a nightmare by those who were left alive. Kept in close captivity inside the mansion-house by the Indians, they were daily tormented by announcements that they were all to be killed *that* day. They were not allowed to show any grief for their lost ones, and they were constantly told that any attempt at rescue would bring their immediate death. They did not know whether to hope for or dread the thought of possible help from the outside world.

"There doesn't seem much to be joyful over," said Mrs. Saunders, one of the survivors, sadly, on Christmas morning, "but I'm going to see if I cannot make some of those white-faced children a little bit happy." So with the small means at her command, she made a feast for them, cooking food that in their present condition seemed like delicacies. It is true that they had to watch their chance to eat when the Indians were not observing them; and it is also true that many were the bitter thoughts and memories that stole away the relish with which they ate the food that kind Mrs. Saunders had so thoughtfully prepared. It was impossible not to contrast the cheer and orderliness of the Whitman home, its singing and reverent observance of Sundays and special days, with this crowded, frightened existence, where each new day dawned with the possibility only that it might hold more of agony and mental suffering than the one before had done.

About noon, they noticed that there was great excitement among the Indians; there was constant running to and fro and much talking and gesticulating. Finally they were told that three boats had arrived at Fort Walla Walla. Who the occupants were was a matter of conjecture, not only to the captives, but evidently to the Indians as well, for the latter at once dispatched a runner to the fort to ascertain if they were friend or foe. That the newcomers had the captives in mind none for an instant doubted. But the captives, having been told that the moment an army should appear from the lower settlements to rescue them, it would be the signal for their death, wavered between the heights of hope and an abyss of terror. The Indians, as well as themselves, were tense with suspense, but it was late afternoon before the messenger returned.

The Indians at once dispatched a runner to the Fort.

This young Indian was much of a tease and loved to play jokes. He knew very well that his tribespeople thought those boats had brought a small army of Americans to rescue the whites, and the opportunity to have a little fun at their expense was too good to be lost. So he rode quietly up to the house and when near the door, began to fire his revolver rapidly, giving vent to vigorous yells at the same time.

One Indian made a dash for his gun and ran out of the mansion, where the refugees had been living, while within and without pandemonium reigned. Then the messenger began to laugh at his excited brethren and enjoyed his joke so well that it was difficult for him to sober down enough to talk. Finally he managed to say between gasps of chuckling and laughter, "They Hudson's Bay boats. The big white chief of Fort Vancouver, he there and he want to have a council with the Cayuses at once."

There was immediate scattering, for every warrior went directly to his tepee to array himself in his bravest attire—that is to say, paint—the vivid reds, whites, and blacks that served to intensify the lines of fierceness and brutality on savage faces.

Late that night they assembled at the mansion, heavily armed and painted for war, looking like so many demons. The whites retired into one room, giving up the rest of the place to them. All their actions were watched apprehensively, for who knew what the next move would be? They demand-

ed food, made sure that all of them had firearms, and finally, mounting their horses, left their prisoners alone.

But the captives were not long in solitude, for runners kept coming and going through the remainder of the night. These would ride up to the door and shout, "News! News!" Having delivered their message, they would rush on again toward the Indian village, or back in the direction of Fort Walla Walla. Then another period of suspenseful silence would ensue.

The whites had little inclination to sleep, for they felt assured that a crisis in their affairs was at hand. Which way would the balance of fate go—

up to life and freedom, or down to an unmarked grave?

The Indian band returned at the end of the following day, in wonderfully high spirits. They reported that a treaty had been made with Mr. Ogden, who was in charge of the Hudson's Bay Company boat.

Tiloukaikt, one of the Indians, was especially jovial and indulged in much laughter and many jokes and tricks on the children. "Big Chief buy you all—everyone but Catherine. He give her to me," he remarked teasingly.

"We'll settle that when we get to the Fort," replied Catherine. "Besides, I couldn't leave Elizabeth."

"She stay too. Big Chief threw her in. In three days you know, for Big Chief say all be there by that time, then he say you belong to me," he answered.

*Three days!* Could it be true? Friends clasped hands, seeing in each other's eyes the thankfulness that none dared express in any but this simple movement. But oh, the unspeakable joy that bounded in every heart!

Preparations were immediately begun for the move. Catherine made another attempt to do some washing for the children. When the captivity had first begun, she had washed some articles of clothing and hung them in the yard, but before they were dry, they had been appropriated by thieving

hands; so, warned by that experience, most of the
small amount of washing done had been dried indoors before the fire. They consoled themselves for
the enforced wearing of garments not often cleaned
by the reflection judiciously voiced by one of their
number, "Dirty clothes is wuth as much to us as
to the pesky Injuns. An' if we kin keep 'em on our
backs, we know where they be, but if we take 'em
off and lay 'em down for five minutes, we're pretty
sartin it ain't *our* backs as will be enjoyin' of 'em
any more."

The cattle were off on the range and Joe Stanfield and the other men had to go after them. "*Do*
get off early, Joe, for it will not give us any too
much time to get there at the end of three days,"
said one of the women. "Maybe you can't find them
as easy as you think."

"I'll have 'em here, don't you worry," answered
Joe easily.

But the women did worry and the hours seemed
very long until in the afternoon of the second day
Stanfield came in from the range with the cattle.
The ever-haunting fear was present in the heart of
each captive that the Indians might suddenly
change their minds and refuse to let them go.

There was no sleep for any of the older portion
of that household of white people that night, for
preparations for departure could not very well be
carried on in the daytime, in the presence of the Indians. The sorting over and selecting from the few

precious things remaining had perforce to be done in the still hours of night. Mercifully, they were left entirely alone that night and a busy time it was.

Some of the women had tried to make sunbonnets for the children to wear, and many were the rents to be patched and mended. Catherine's concern was chiefly for her little sisters, though she took time to carefully count and restore to its hiding place in Mother Whitman's tin coffee can, her one treasure —a small amount of money. This money had been earned, a few cents at a time, by the sale of produce from her garden. The Whitmans had permitted each child to have a small plot of ground to care for and they kept for their own whatever they could get by selling their vegetables to the emigrants.

Breakfast was prepared and eaten before light on the following morning and before the day had fairly begun the loading into three emigrant wagons was accomplished and the haggard-looking occupants had started on their way to liberty and safety. The last wagon held Mrs. Saunders and her children, the Youngs, Eliza, and the four Sager girls. A chair had been placed in the front end and on it sat Catherine, holding Henrietta, feeble from her long siege of measles and the enforced discomfort of the last five weeks. The rest of the party were perched, wherever a resting place might be found, on the piles of bedding and the belongings they were taking with them. Of these there was a considerable quantity, but more had been left behind.

Some few of the chiefs accompanied them, but they did not remain very near them, going ahead on their wiry little ponies.

Each wagon was drawn by three yokes of oxen, that number being necessary to haul them through the mud of the trail. It was the 29th of December, and as the children turned regretful eyes upon their only pets, numerous cats and kittens, which they were forced to leave behind, faint rays of early sunshine crept through the mist and illumined the place where they had passed so many miserable days in weary captivity. Their last glimpse of it, bathed in winter sunshine, with the pussies near

They gave one last look at the
Whitman Mission.

the door calmly washing their faces, unmindful
that their friends were leaving them forever, made
a picture in sharp contrast to what met their eyes
as they turned their heads in the other direction—
the partly wrecked Mission house and not very
far from it, the low mound that had become the last
resting place of so many of their loved ones.

The Doctor's house, standing there grim and
desolate, told its own mute tale of disaster, and
tears came hot and fast to their eyes. It did not
need the evidence of the doorless and windowless
house, through whose openings they could discover
the confusion of broken furniture and smashed
stoves, covered with feathers ripped from beds and
settee cushions, to remind the children that their
happy, sheltered life under the guidance and teaching of their two devoted friends was forever at an
end and that they were facing an existence whose
faintest outline they could not at the moment
perceive.

But, as always, the Sager children, whose lives
had been so full of adventurous happenings, found
kind friends, ready and glad to help them. First at
Fort Vancouver and later at Oregon City they
were received with kindness, and finally adopted
into homes of kindly people there, where they grew
up to live happy and useful lives.